To
Happy Xmas 2003
Love McCrabbs
xxxxx

Amazing Facts about Australian Frogs and Reptiles

Text by Pat Slater

Steve Parish
DISCOVER & LEARN
ABOUT AUSTRALIA
www.steveparish.com.au

Contents

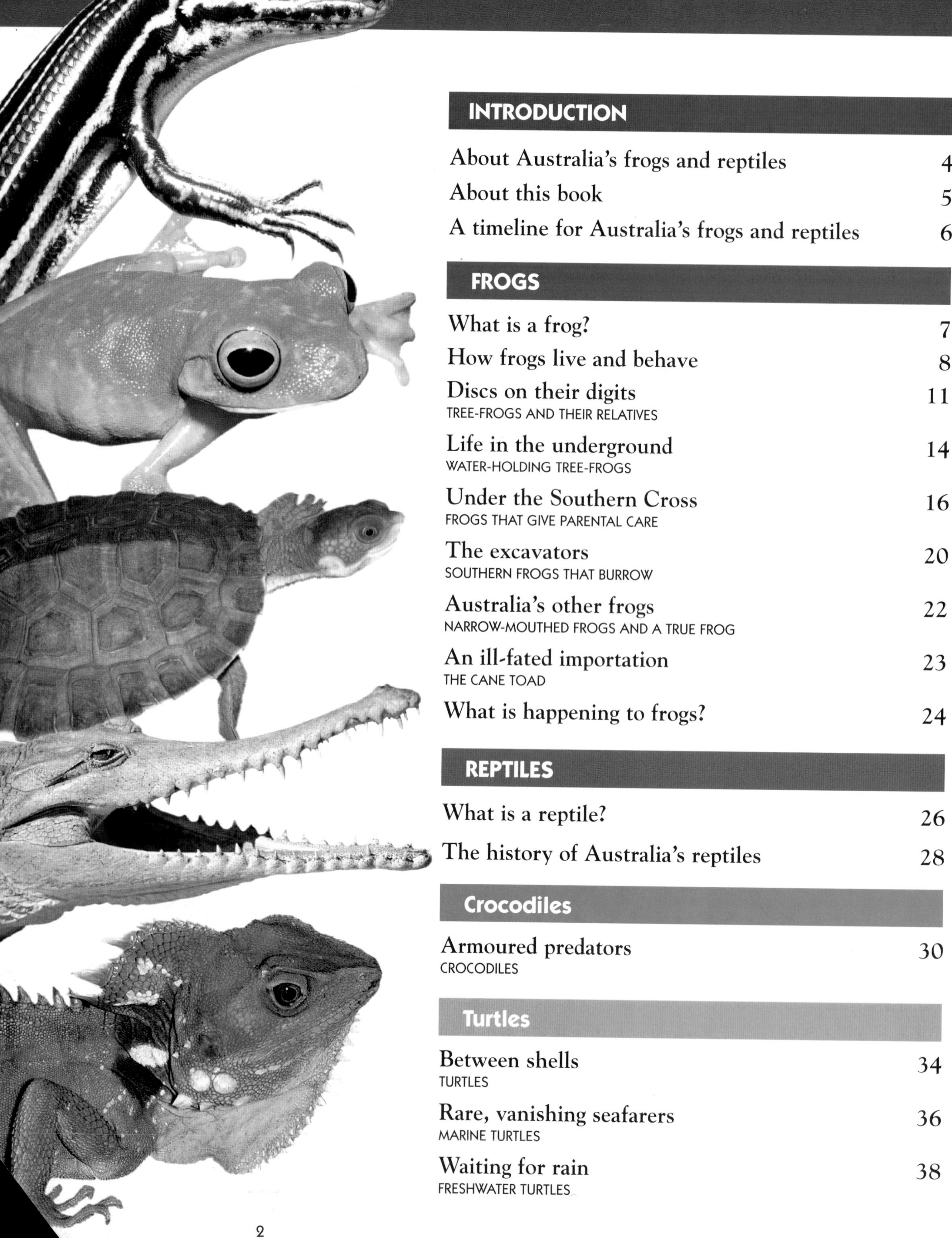

Lizards

Snakes

MAKING MORE DISCOVERIES

About Australia's frogs and reptiles

STANLEY BREEDEN

Mertens' Water Monitor lives near Australia's tropical waterways and in wetlands

Australia's frogs and reptiles are beautiful and remarkable creatures. Many of them are found nowhere else in the world.

The ancestors of some of these frogs and reptiles lived in Australia when it was still part of the supercontinent Gondwana. When Australia finally became separated from Antarctica, it drifted northwards, carrying its cargo of animals. Over long ages, the continent became drier. Some frogs and reptiles remained in the shrinking rainforests. Others adapted to live in the growing desert regions and in areas suffering seasonal drought. As the landmass neared Asia, new frogs and reptiles arrived, travelling over a later-submerged land bridge, or drifting to shore on flotsam.

JIRI LOCHMAN

The Three-lined Knob-tailed Gecko, like many other Australian reptiles, is adapted to living in arid areas

The Dainty Green Tree-frog may live in a garden

JIRI LOCHMAN

The Green Turtle, like all marine turtles, needs protection

About this book

This book gives an observer's overview of Australia's frogs and reptiles. There are too many species to mention all of them by name, but as you read this book you will discover interesting facts about members of all the major groups.

You will find pictures of many of the most remarkable species, taken by leading nature photographers. The Index inside the back cover will give ready reference to the species pictured. The **facts** columns will add to your knowledge of the animals pictured and their relations. More about words marked with an asterisk (*) in the text can be found in the Glossary on page 79. Some further reading is listed on page 80 but you may wish to visit your local library to consult other reference books.

Welcome to the world of Australia's frogs and reptiles.

Eastern Bearded Dragon, scientific name *Pogona barbata*

IAN MORRIS

The Northern Death Adder kills its prey by injecting venom* into its tissues

Naming animals

An animal has a common name, which changes from place to place, and a scientific name, which remains the same all over the world.

The scientific name is written in italics. The first word, the genus*, places the creature in a group of closely related animals. The second name, the species*, belongs only to that animal and to others with which it could mate and produce fertile offspring.

DID YOU KNOW?

FACTS

- The giant "megafauna", which existed in Australia until around 30 000, or fewer, years ago, included *Megalania,* a goanna 6 m long, *Quinkana*, a land crocodile 3 m long and *Wonambi*, a python 6 m long.
- A fossil* is the trace of something which was once alive. It may be an imprint, or a cast made when living tissue was replaced by stone.
- Often a frog fossil is only a single fragile bone found with other animal fossils. The earliest Australian frog fossil, found at Murgon, Qld, has been dated to around 54.5 million years ago.
- The labyrinthodonts*, which gave rise to modern amphibians, were named because of the crinkled outer and inner surfaces of their teeth.

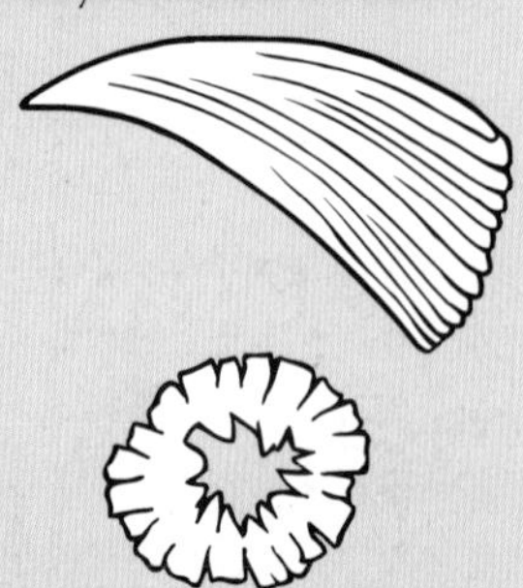

A timeline for Australia's frogs and reptiles

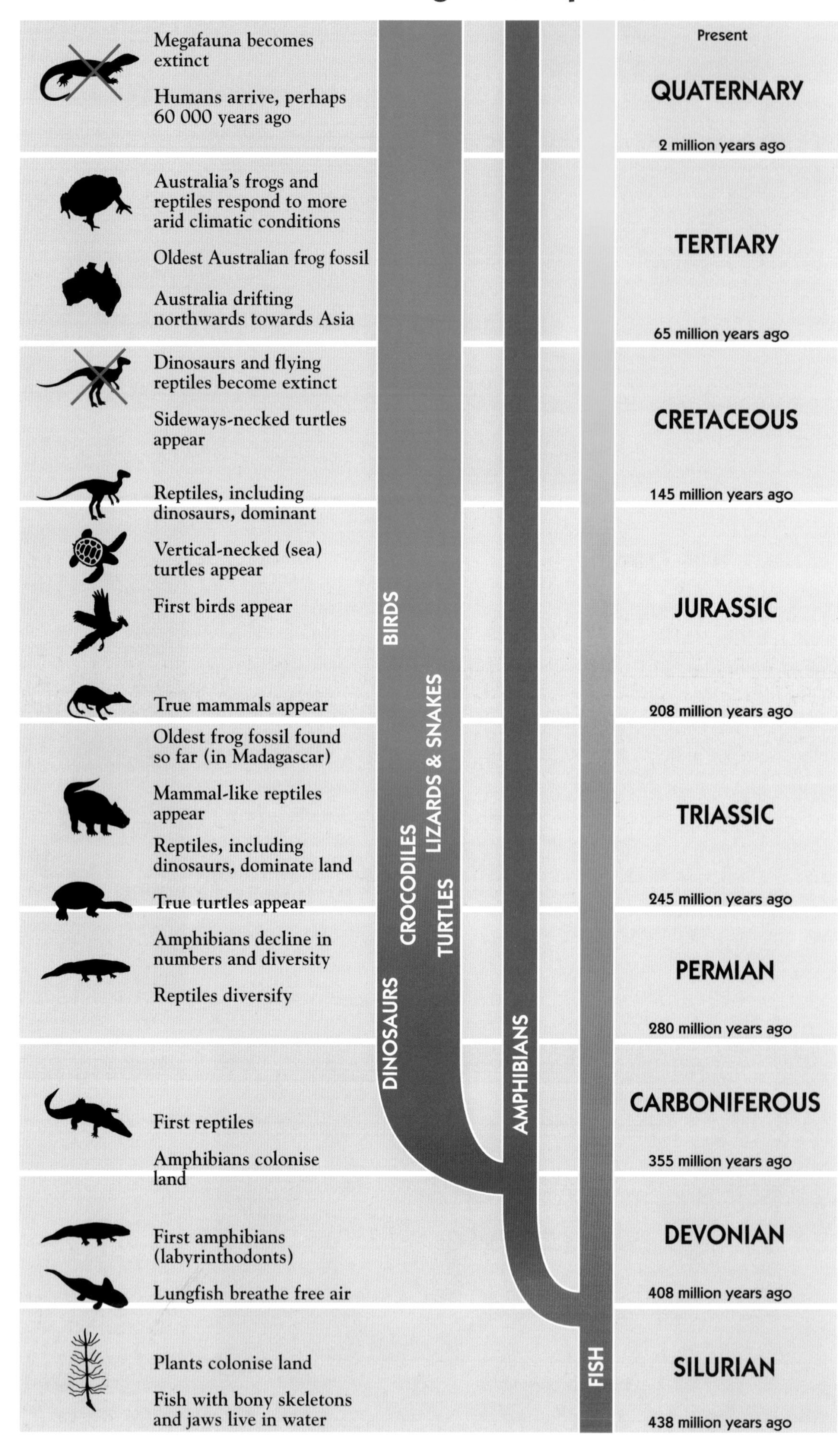

What is a frog?

The Dainty Green Tree-frog of coastal northeastern Australia

A frog is a vertebrate* animal. Like reptiles, birds and mammals*, adult frogs have backbones, and their brains are protected by skulls. Like reptiles, frogs are "cold-blooded" (ectothermic*) animals, whose body temperatures are influenced by the temperature of their surroundings.

A frog is an amphibian*, "an animal with two ways of living", in water and on land. It has moist, glandular* skin which may act as a breathing organ. Frog eggs do not have hard shells, and are laid in water or in damp places. The tadpole which hatches from each egg is tailed, limbless, mainly vegetarian* and breathes through gills*. As it matures, it grows limbs, absorbs its tail, loses its gills, and develops lungs. It undergoes metamorphosis* into an air-breathing, land-living, tailless adult which eats small animals.

Frogs are the only amphibians found naturally in Australia (toads are not native here). Salamanders, mud puppies, newts, and wormlike caecilians are amphibians found in other parts of the world.

SOME PARTS OF A FROG

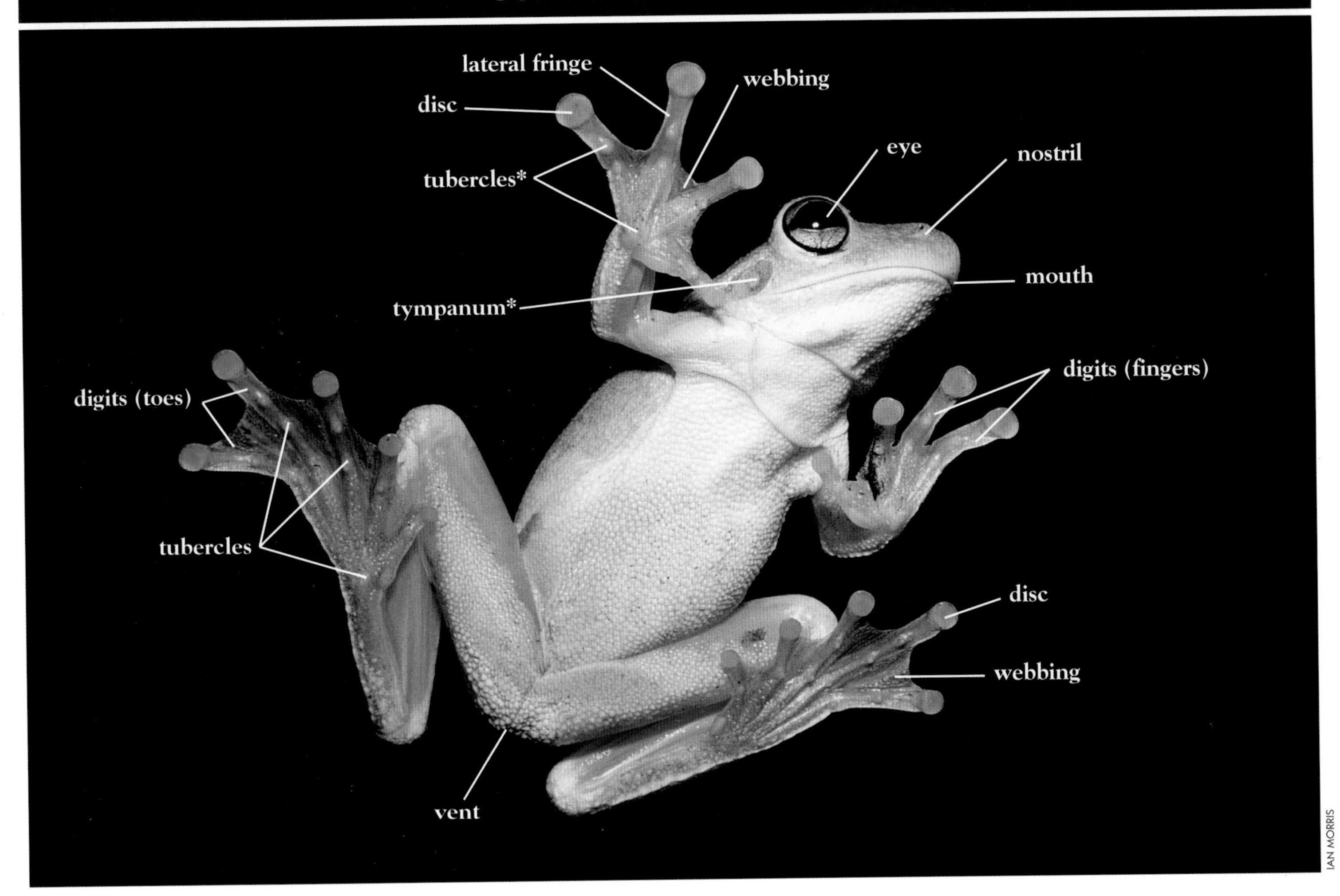

How frogs live and behave

Staying damp

Frogs have developed many strategies for resisting water loss from their bodies.

Their blood contains a chemical which slows dehydration*. They live in damp places, retreat to water as often as possible, shelter from heat and are active at night. During hot and dry conditions, some species burrow and aestivate*. Arid-country frogs have brief egg and tadpole stages.

Some species of Australian frogs which live in the Victorian Alps are active in temperatures approaching freezing point.

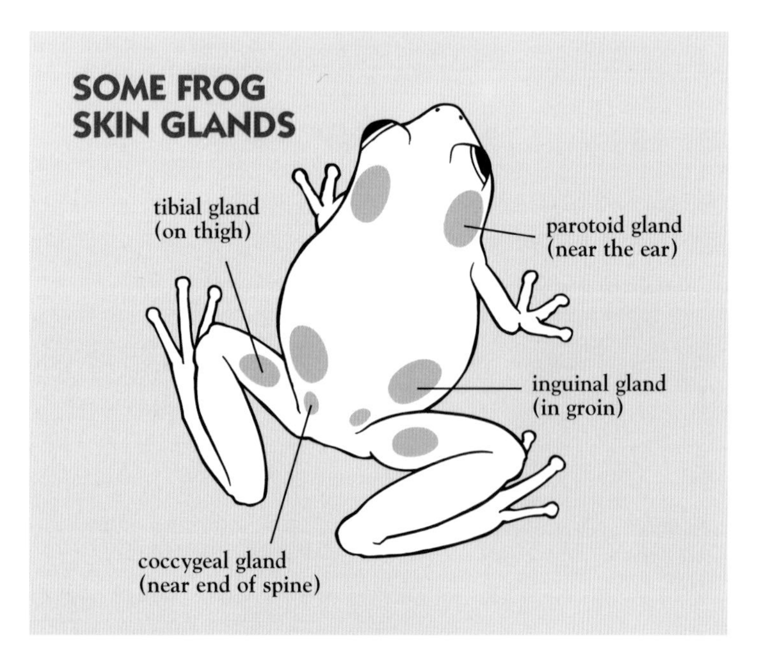

Frog legs *à la carte*

Frogs provide food for many other animals, such as snakes, birds and small carnivorous* mammals.

Humans find them tasty also. By the nineteenth century, the French were eating frog legs with enthusiasm and as their own Edible Frog disappeared they imported supplies. In 1977 the French government banned hunting its own frogs. Other European supplies had dried up, so frogs were obtained from India and Bangladesh. The USA imported more than 6.5 million pounds (three million kilograms) of frozen legs *each year* between 1981 and 1984. At present the USA, Germany, the Netherlands and France are top importers of frog legs. Asia supplies most of today's demand.

This Tschudi's Froglet is hunting insects while remaining in the water

Chemical protection

The skin of all frogs contains glands. Some help keep the skin moist, others secrete substances which may act as fungicides or antibiotics.

In some frog species the glands are large (the positions of some glands are shown at left). They may produce nasty-tasting or poisonous secretions to repel predators*, and the owner of such glands often displays warning colours of red, orange or yellow and black to advertise that it is not good to eat. Glands on the shoulders of the Cane Toad produce a poisonous fluid which can be squirted some distance.

Wash your hands after touching any frog!

Many animals, such as this Keelback or Freshwater Snake, eat frogs

IAN MORRIS

This Northern Snapping Frog is eating a smaller frog of its own species

Grab - gulp!

Frogs usually prey on insects and other small invertebrates*, though large species may eat reptiles, small mammals and other frogs. They hunt by sight and most take only moving, live animals.

A frog's tongue is attached at its front end, and is flipped out at prey. Its upper surface, coated with sticky secretion, traps the victim, which is flopped back into the mouth, is swallowed alive and dies of suffocation in the frog's stomach. Large prey may be pushed in with the hands.

Some frogs have no teeth, others do, and almost all have spikes called vomerine* teeth growing from the roof of the mouth. The teeth are used to hold prey.

INSIDE A FROG'S MOUTH

vomerine teeth
upper jawbone
opening to nostril
bulge made by underside of eyeball
opening to larynx
tongue
lower jawbone
tongue fastens here

TWO WAYS A FROG MAY BREATHE

nostrils
air out
mouth cavity
lungs
(a)
air in
glottis*
(b)
(c)
air in and out
glottis
(d)

(a) to (c) Air passes out from the lungs through the open glottis and nostrils. Then the glottis closes and the floor of the mouth descends, drawing air through the nostrils into the mouth. Finally, the nostrils close, the glottis opens and air passes into the lungs, where gas exchange takes place.

(d) Air may be pumped in and out through the nostrils as the floor of the mouth is lowered then raised. Gas exchange takes place in the lining of the mouth.

FACTS

- Australia has 220 or more of the world's more than 2000 frogs and toads.
- Australia has no native toads, though some small burrowing frogs are called "toadlets".
- The first Australian frog seen in Europe was a Green Tree-frog collected by Sir Joseph Banks during his voyage with Captain Cook in 1770. The specimen was destroyed by a bomb which fell on London during World War 2.
- One-third of Australia's frogs burrow to escape dry conditions.
- Most frogs can lighten or darken their skin colour by spacing out or clumping together tiny grains of black pigment* in the skin.
- Camouflage devices used by frogs include skin colour, skin pattern and flaps of skin which disguise the outline. A mask of dark skin may hide the eyes.
- Some frogs have "flash markings", brilliant colours on hindlegs, groins or sides. These startle a predator as the frog jumps away.
- The introduced Cane Toad will take prey that does not move (including dog food and cigarette butts).

DID YOU KNOW?

FACTS

- Male frogs develop breeding pads or spikes on their hands. These are used to grasp females, then are shed when the skin is moulted.
- A female frog will respond only to calls made by males of her own species.
- If a female frog is clasped by a male but has already laid, she makes a special "release" call.
- The young of some frog species develop direct from egg to froglet inside the egg capsule, without going through a tadpole stage.
- If the jelly which surrounds frog eggs is removed, they cannot be fertilised. It is thought to contain a vital hormone.

IAN MORRIS

Green Tree-frogs in amplexus. The black caps on the eggs give protection against ultraviolet rays

Making more frogs

During the breeding season, a male frog finds a likely site and advertises for a mate by calling.

He grasps the female from behind in an embrace called amplexus* and sheds sperm on the eggs as they leave her body. The eggs are surrounded by material which, on contacting water, swells to a protective jelly. This jelly and the fertilised eggs form frog spawn. The tadpoles which hatch from the eggs are vegetarian and breathe through gills.

A tadpole's limbs all develop at the same time, but the front legs emerge after the hindlegs. One front leg pushes through a gill slit; the other one emerges through the skin on the opposite side of the body. The tail is absorbed.

The adult frog is carnivorous, and it breathes through its lungs and skin rather than through gills.

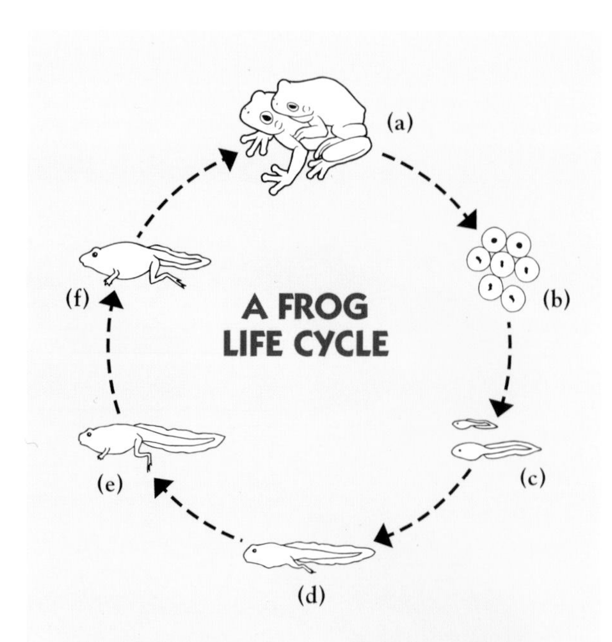

(a) Adult frogs mate
(b) Eggs hatch
(c) Tadpoles grow
(d) Hind legs develop
(e) Front leg emerges
(f) Other front leg emerges. Then the tail is absorbed, the lungs develop and finally the frog leaves the water

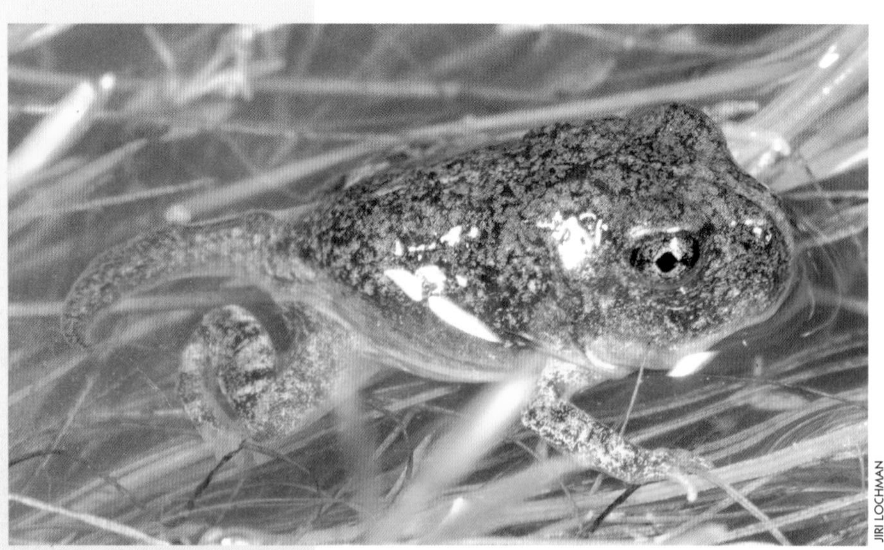
JIRI LOCHMAN

This advanced tadpole of the Humming Frog has four limbs active and is rapidly absorbing its tail

Discs on their digits

Members of the tree-frog family are found in many parts of the world.

Although there are many different shapes and sizes of frogs within the family, every tree-frog has a small piece of cartilage* between the final two bones of each finger and toe. This is called an intercalary* structure.

The Australian tree-frogs are divided into three major groups:

- **A large group of climbing tree-frogs.**
- **A small group of rocket-frogs**, which live on the ground and are mighty leapers.
- **Another large group, the water-holding frogs. These** are plump-bodied burrowers, which can store water in their bodies and use it during dry times.

Blue Mountains Tree-frog. At rest, its drawn-up legs conceal the bright colours of its sides and thighs

IAN MORRIS

Sticky fingers

Climbing tree-frogs have round, adhesive discs at the ends of their digits. There are about 50 species known in Australia so far. They are most abundant around the well watered northern and eastern coasts of the continent. These frogs are often brightly coloured, but they are well camouflaged in vegetation. Many species can make their skin lighter or darker. When resting, they tuck their arms and legs against their sides, hands and feet under their bodies, then flatten themselves, so they cast little shadow.

FACTS

- At least four species of tree-frogs "talk" with their limbs, behaviour known as "foot-flagging". This may be male versus male aggression.

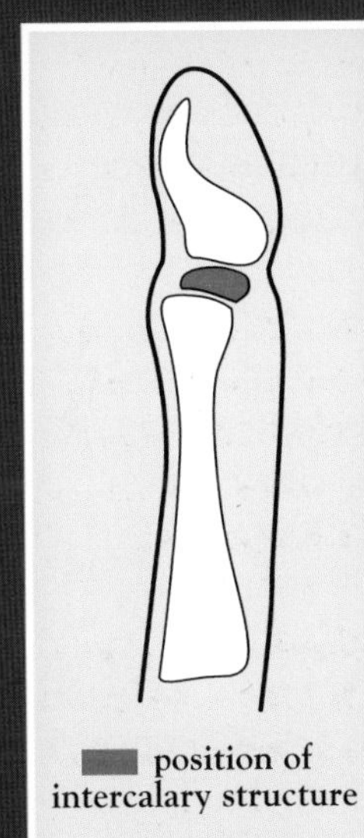

Diagrammatic cross-section of tree-frog toe

The White-lipped Tree-frog, Australia's largest frog, can grow to nearly 14 cm in length. Its call sounds like a dog barking

PETER MARSACK

Moore's Frog, found near water in southwest WA, is active by day

DID YOU KNOW?

FACTS

- The Northern Water Frog of the Top End and the Gulf of Carpentaria can release slimy mucus from its skin glands. This makes the frog difficult for predators to grasp.
- The call of the male Roth's Tree-frog resembles maniacal laughter. This frog occurs in coastal wetland from Cooloola, Qld, to Broome, WA.
- The Magnificent Tree-frog of the Kimberley, WA, was unknown to science until 1977. It lives in caves, but has been found in public camping spots, where toilets form cool hiding places.
- The Naked (or Red) Tree-frog is found in the northern three-quarters of Australia.

IAN MORRIS

The Northern Water Frog lives on floodplains. Unlike most other frogs, it can feed underwater

STANLEY BREEDEN

The Australian Lace-lid lives in Cape York rainforest. It probably came from New Guinea

Belly-drinking

Frogs do not drink through their mouths. Apart from a small amount of moisture from their food, they obtain nearly all their water requirements by taking in liquid through the skin on their undersides. The water passes into spaces called lymph sacs, then into the bloodstream.

The skin of the undersurface and hindlimbs of a tree-frog is granular*, which increases the surface area available to absorb water. Some of the tree-frogs have waterproof skin on their upper surfaces. This reduces the loss of water from the body when the frog snuggles onto a surface.

DAYTIME CAMOUFLAGE AND NIGHT-TIME ACTIVITY

Roth's Tree-frog resting in the shade during the day

Laughing Tree-frog calling on a branch at night

JIRII LOCHMAN

In arid country, the Naked Tree-frog spawns in temporary pools

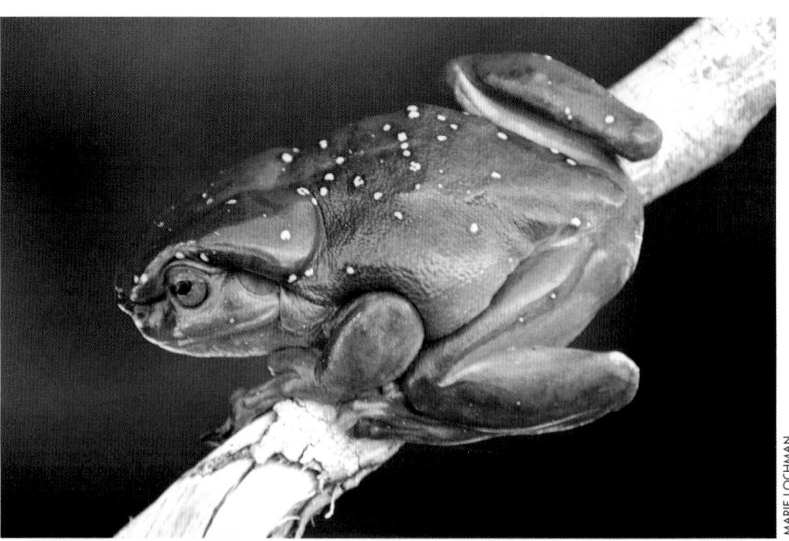

MARIE LOCHMAN

The Magnificent Tree-frog can grow to 10.6 cm in length

Glands form bumps over the Green Tree-frog's eyes

The tiny Rockhole Frog "walks on water"

IAN MORRIS

Homing Green Tree-frogs

The Green Tree-frog grows up to 11 centimetres in length and lives in the northern and northeastern parts of Australia. It often enters houses. This frog has a well-developed "homing" instinct. Remove one from its usual roost and take it some distance away and it usually returns.

An Emerald-spotted Tree-frog displays its discs

Climbing and clinging

Tree-frogs can climb very slick surfaces, including glass. On the undersurface of the disc on the frog's digit is a pattern of interlocking six-sided cells with gaps between them (rather like the non-slip pattern on the soles of people's sports shoes). These cells probably interlock with tiny projections from the surface upon which the frog moves or rests. A frog clinging to a smooth, upright surface flattens itself. Moisture on its belly bonds with moisture on the surface, helping hold the frog in place.

IAN MORRIS

The Javelin Frog of northern Australia is 1.5 cm long

Streamlined leapers

The second group of tree-frogs, the rocket-frogs, are usually seen on the ground. They have pointy snouts, smaller finger and toe discs, and longer, stronger hindlegs than their climbing relatives. The longest legs in this group belong to the Striped Rocket-frog, found in wetlands in northeastern and northern Australia.

FACTS

- The tiny Rockhole Frog of the Kimberley and Arnhem Land, sometimes called the "Jesus Christ" frog, skitters across water without breaking the surface film. It moves fast, weighs little and skips across the water at a low angle, like a skimming stone.
- The glands on the head of the Green Tree-frog produce a drug which controls blood pressure in humans. This drug is now made synthetically.
- In the USA, the Green Tree-frog is bred for the pet trade. Frogs are not easy to keep, as they require live food. However, one Green Tree-frog lived in captivity for 23 years.

IAN MORRIS

A male Striped Rocket-frog calling for a mate.
This frog is a super leaper

FACTS ABOUT BURROWING FROGS

- Burrowing frogs have broad heads, rounded bodies and short, sturdy limbs.
  Some species descend into moist or sandy soil at an angle backwards, digging with their hindfeet. Other burrowing frogs sink straight down, digging with their feet while turning slowly in a circle.
  Only two species burrow with their hands and descend headfirst. The Turtle Frog (see p.20) and the Sandhill Frog (see p. 21) have spade-like hands and pads on their noses.

WATER-HOLDING TREE-FROGS

Life in the underground

The third group of tree-frogs, found in the north and the arid Red Centre of Australia, is called the *Cyclorana*. This means "round-frogs", and these frogs are squat-bodied burrowers, which may spend long dry periods underground. Before they "sleep", they store water within their bodies, then, as they dehydrate, they reabsorb some of the water.

A water-holding frog lacks discs on its fingers and toes, though it has the intercalary structures that lead to it being placed in the tree-frog group. The first finger of the hand is opposed to the other three (in the same way as a human thumb is opposed to the other four fingers). These frogs' hind-legs are muscular, and each foot has a sharp spade-like prominence for digging.

Most species of water-holding frogs have dull, mottled, earth-toned markings, which may brighten at breeding time.

IAN MORRIS

When Northern Snapping Frogs are ready to breed, their markings become brighter

Sleeping underground

The water-holding frogs, and many other Australian frogs as well, survive long periods of dry weather by aestivating underground.

The frog stores water in its bladder, then digs down into the ground, pushing the soil sideways as it is dug away. At the end of the shaft, the frog aestivates, in a chamber just larger than its body. It is surrounded by a cocoon of several layers of dead skin, unbroken except where the nostrils connect to the outside through little tubes. This cocoon reduces water loss. A frog without a cocoon of dead skin loses around seven and one-half times the amount of water lost by a frog protected by a cocoon. After rain, the frog comes to the surface, absorbs water, sheds its cocoon, feeds and breeds.

Burrowing frogs emerging after drought possibly account for stories of "frogs falling from the sky" with rain.

Frogs can conserve water by huddling together. When five frogs cluster together, the water loss for each frog is about half what it would be if the frog were alone.

IAN MORRIS

The Long-footed Frog's call sounds like the drawn-out moo of a cow

LIVING WATER-BOTTLES

PETER SLATER

This Water-holding Frog is about to shed its cocoon

JIRI LOCHMAN

... now, the frog is ready to feed and breed

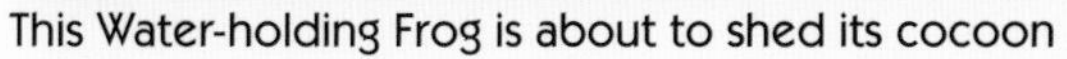

The species known as the Water-holding Frog was a traditional source of moisture for human desert travellers. They dug the frog from its burrow near a dried-up waterhole, then squeezed out the water stored in its body and swallowed it. The frog was then eaten. Many burrowing frogs produce dilute urine, consisting of a small amount of waste material in a large amount of water. In some of these frogs, the weight of water which can be held in the bladder is about the same as the original body weight of the animal. When the frog aestivates, it uses its bladder as a storage tank. If it becomes dehydrated, it reabsorbs water.

FACTS

- The Northern Snapping Frog (see photo on p. 9) may be 10.5 cm in length. Its tadpole may be 7 cm long.
- The Northern Snapping Frog emerges from its burrow after rain. It will eat any animal it can swallow, including other frogs. Even in hot weather, it may bask in the sun near water.
- Male water-holding frogs often call from inside their burrows.

Changing skins

As often as once per week, an active frog of any species sheds the outer, dead layer of its skin, exposing a fresh layer underneath.

To shed its skin, the frog arches its body, breathes heavily in and out, opens and shuts its mouth and eyes, and scrapes at its head and body with hands and feet. Eventually it tears holes in the old skin and manages to grab it at one side. The frog uses its hands to drag the skin off and to stuff the material into its mouth. Then it swallows it. This process usually takes about an hour to complete.

The cocoon which surrounds a burrowing frog, formed from outer layers of its skin, is torn off and swallowed in this way after the frog emerges from underground. Then the frog hunts for its usual prey.

IAN MORRIS

The Long-footed Frog of northern Australia emerges from its burrow to breed early in the Wet season

Under the Southern Cross

Carpenter Frog

IAN MORRIS

Over half the Australian species of frogs belong to the southern frogs, a family of frogs found only in the Southern Hemisphere.

Australia has around 20 different groups of southern frogs. These groups vary widely in appearance, lifestyle and breeding habits, but their skeletons have similar features. Some have expanded toe tips, but no southern frog has the digit discs typical of climbing tree-frogs. They are also similar in that they "look after" their eggs and sometimes their tadpoles.

Southern frogs range from tiny froglets, which may be only 13 millimetres in length, to the bulky barred frogs, which may reach 10 centimetres. Southern frogs may have powerful leaping limbs, or tiny limbs which force them to waddle or run rather than hop. Some climb, some live on the ground or in water and some are burrowers. They lay their eggs in a variety of situations – in still or moving water, in floating nests of foam, on the ground amongst leaf litter, or even in burrows.

JIRI LOCHMAN

Glauert's Froglet is common in coastal southwest WA

Pobblebonk!

The scientific name of one group of southern frogs, *Limnodynastes*, means "Lord of the marshes". These marsh frogs include two species called "banjo frogs" or "pobblebonks", because of their hollow, resounding calls.

While mating, a female *Limnodynastes* frog paddles on the surface with her hands, trapping air bubbles, which she throws downwards and backwards under her body. Her eggs, surrounded by egg jelly, are fertilised by the male's sperm, then become caught in the raft of bubbles. This suspends them just under the surface of the water until they hatch.

JIRI LOCHMAN

Two Western Banjo Frogs, one of them burrowing

The Striped Marsh-frog grows to 7.3 cm

DID YOU KNOW?

FACTS

- The Carpenter Frog has a very large tympanum. It is the only known member of a group of southern frogs whose scientific name, *Megistolotis*, means "largest ear".
- The Carpenter Frog lives in rocky outcrops in northern Australia. Its call is a soft tapping noise, like a hammer striking timber.
- Some marsh frogs have a large gland on the calf of each hind leg. These glands produce a creamy substance which predators find nasty-tasting and which may be poisonous.
- The Striped Marsh-frog can be found in coastal swamps from Cape York to SE South Australia. The eggs are laid in still water, in a foam nest.

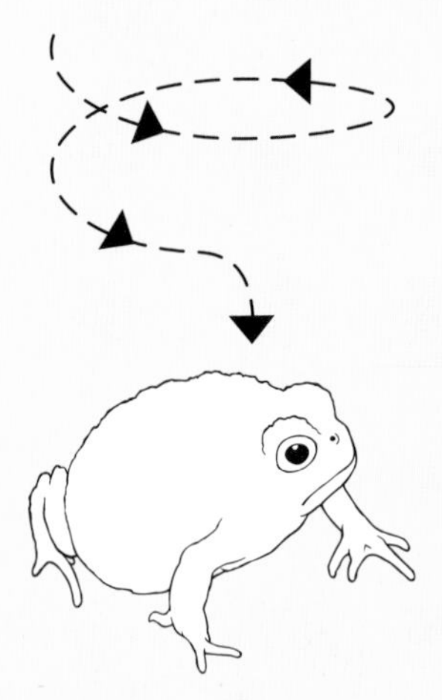

A spadefoot frog corkscrews down into the ground, digging with sharp-edged tubercles under its feet

The Northern Banjo Frog grows to 7.9 cm. It lives in woodland and rainforest from Cape York to northern NSW

Red-and-yellow

The colourful Red-and-yellow Mountain-frog lives in the McPherson Ranges of southeastern Queensland and northeastern New South Wales. Its large eggs are laid in a pool under a rock. The tadpoles survive on their egg-yolks, and do not feed before changing into adult frogs.

OWEN KELLY

The Red-and-yellow Mountain-frog is a rainforest species

Battling tuskers

Both male and female Tusked Frogs have a pair of pointed, bony teeth called tusks at the front of the lower jaw.

The male is larger than the female (which is unusual among frogs) and has a massive head compared to the size of its body. Battling males try to seize each other's head in their jaws, then hang on with determination. The eggs are laid in a floating foam nest. After fertilising them, the male remains with the nest until the tadpoles hatch.

IAN MORRIS

The male Tusked Frog uses his tusks to fight with other males

FACTS ABOUT FROGLETS

- Tiny, perfectly formed frogs may not be young frogs at all, but adults of the group *Crinia,* usually known as "froglets".
- All species of *Crinia* froglets live close to water, because they are so small (about 2 cm in length) that they dehydrate easily.
- There are 18 species of Australian froglets. Even members of the same species can vary widely in colour and skin texture. The best way to tell species apart is by their calls.
- Glauert's Froglet may grow to 2.4 cm in length and is found in coastal southwest WA, westwards to Esperance. Adults are common, but the tadpole is unknown. This tiny frog's call has been likened to the rattle of dry peas in a can.
- Tschudi's Froglet (photo p. 8) occurs in the high rainfall zone of coastal southwest WA. It grows to 3.6 cm in length and the male's call is a loud "quack ... quack".

DID YOU KNOW?

FACTS

- The Southern Gastric-brooding Frog has a particularly short snout. Its scientific name, *Rheobatrachus silus,* means "pug-nosed stream-frog".
- Gastric-brooding frogs spend most of their time in the water. They have large hindlegs with webbed toes.
- The gastric-brooding frogs have tongues which cannot be flicked out of their mouths. They probably lunge open-mouthed at insects floating on the surface of the water.
- While a gastric-brooding frog's stomach contains tadpoles, it stops producing harmful hydrochloric acid. The substance which shuts off the acid has been reproduced and is used to treat human stomach ulcers.
- The Northern Gastric-brooding Frog is found higher than 400 m above sea level, the Southern Gastric-brooding Frog higher than 300 m above sea level.

Growing up inside mother

The remarkable Southern Gastric-brooding Frog was discovered in 1973, in a small area of mountain rainforest in the Conondale Ranges in southeastern Queensland. A larger relative, the Northern Gastric-brooding Frog was discovered in 1984, in rainforest in the Clarke Range, near Mackay. The females of these species swallow their fertilised eggs. Up to 25 tadpoles then develop into frogs in each mother's stomach.

The Southern Gastric-brooding Frog, not seen since 1981

OWEN KELLY

The tadpoles spend up to six weeks in their nursery, nourished by their large yolk sacs. As they grow, they can take up so much space that their mother's lungs collapse and she has to breathe through her skin. Finally, fully developed little frogs, they are "born" through the mother's mouth over a period lasting as long as a week. Each baby climbs up its mother's gullet, sits on her tongue, then steps out into the world through her wide-opened jaws.

The Southern Gastric-brooding Frog has not been seen since 1981. The Northern Gastric-brooding Frog has not been seen since 1985. Some scientists think a virus affecting frogs which live in high rainforest streams at some altitude above sea level may be responsible for the disappearances.

Up to 20 tadpoles may spend up to six weeks in the stomach of the female Northern Gastric-brooding Frog

Body language

Six species of day-frog live in fast-flowing rainforest creeks in coastal northeastern Australia. Most day-frog species are considered rare or endangered. The Southern Day-frog was last seen in the wild in 1979.

The male Southern Day-frog does not have a vocal sac, and his call is a gentle rattling, unlikely to be heard over rushing water. One frog of this species will signal another by stretching and waving the arms and legs while making tiny hops. The waving frog will gradually approach the other one, then make contact with hands and chin. This is thought to be courtship behaviour.

The Southern Day-frog was last seen in January, 1979

Frogs in the moss

The Corroboree Frog is about three centimetres in length. The rather bumpy skin of its back is yellow or greenish-yellow, striped with black. Its name was given because of a fancied resemblance to the body-painting used by Aboriginal people for their ceremonies.

This striking frog lives in bogs of sphagnum moss in the Australian Alps and appears to feed on ants and mites. Breeding takes place from December to April. Between 12 and 30 eggs are laid in moist sphagnum moss, and the tadpoles take up to 30 weeks to complete development inside their egg capsules. One of the parents stays with the eggs during this time.

The Corroboree Frog lives in bogs of sphagnum moss in the Australian Alps

Hip-pocket babies

The male Marsupial Frog has a "hip pocket" on each of his sides. After between eight and 18 eggs are laid and fertilised, the male stays near them for 11 days until they hatch. Egg jelly becomes smeared on the male's skin, and the tadpoles wriggle through the jelly, up his sides and into a "pouch". There they remain for between seven and ten weeks before emerging as tiny frogs. This frog lives in rainforest in southeastern Queensland and northeastern New South Wales.

▶ The Jabiru Toadlet is known only from one part of Kakadu National Park, NT.

Jabiru Toadlet

DID YOU KNOW?

FACTS ABOUT BURROWING FROGS

- About 25% of Australian frog species lay their eggs out of water. The tadpoles either mature in the egg capsule on land, or enter the water when well developed.
- The Turtle Frog of Western Australia looks like a tiny turtle without a shell. A courting pair will burrow into the sand. At a depth of about 1 m, they lay and fertilise eggs, which develop into tadpoles underground.
- A Turtle Frog was seen to eat 474 termites in one meal.

Ornate Burrowing Frog

- Australia's burrowing frogs are still being discovered. In 1980, there were only two species of the tiny burrowing *Uperoleia* frogs, or "gungans", known. By 1993 there were 24.

The excavators

The Western Spotted Frog is found in southwestern WA

JIRI LOCHMAN

Spikes on their thumbs

***Heleioporus* frogs are large, plump and bumpy-skinned. Males of most species grow black spikes on their thumbs each breeding season. The spikes are used to hold the females while mating, then they are shed with the skin. The presence of a *Heleioporus* frog may be betrayed by the deep, repeated call given by the male at the entrance to his burrow, or from underground. After a female responds and they mate, the fertilised eggs remain in a nest of foam in the burrow. They do not hatch until rain floods the burrow.**

Five *Heleioporus* species live in southwestern Western Australia. The Giant Burrowing Frog, a big, dark frog with yellow spots along its sides, lives in coastal New South Wales and northern Victoria. It was first described in 1795.

Heleioporus burrowing frogs are sometimes mistaken for Cane Toads. However, *Heleioporus* frogs have vertical pupils in their eyes (the Cane Toad has horizontal pupils). They do not have enlarged, poison-containing glands on their shoulders, and their skin does not have the leathery texture of toad skin.

JIRI LOCHMAN

The male Spencer's Burrowing Frog calls to attract females while floating in a pool

JIRI LOCHMAN

Sandhill Frog

Frogs in the sandhills

In 1970, ten small, round-bodied, short-legged frogs fell into traps dug to catch mammals in coastal sandhills at Shark Bay, Western Australia. The frogs had broad, short-fingered hands and in some ways resembled the burrowing Turtle Frog. The species was named the Sandhill Frog. In 1979, detective work carried out by scientists in the desolate sand dunes at False Entrance Well Tank, on Carrarang Station, Shark Bay, discovered its lifestyle.

The Sandhill Frog burrows into the sand at dawn, diving in head first, digging with its hands until it can push itself further down with its hindfeet. The surface sand is dry, but 10 centimetres down it is damp. Once the buried frog reaches this layer, it can absorb moisture through its skin. At night, the frog emerges and hunts ants and other insects across the surface of the dunes.

Sandhill Frogs form pairs during winter. Mates remain below the surface together for at least five months. As the sand dries, they burrow further down, sometimes to 80 centimetres. Between six and 11 white eggs are laid and fertilised underground. The tadpoles develop into frogs inside their egg capsules.

The Trilling Frog lives in arid grassland

IAN MORRIS

Male Northern Spadefoot Frog calling

Red spots mean BEWARE

The small burrowing "spadefoot frogs" have warty skins dotted with red, yellow or orange. After rain, huge numbers come to the surface, shed their cocoons, feed on ants and termites and look for mates. Round-bodied and with short legs, they run like fat mice rather than hop.

The scientific name of the spadefoot frogs is *Notaden*, meaning "back gland". When such a frog is handled, creamy liquid comes from its skin. This may be poisonous and the frog's markings may signal the fact to predators.

IAN MORRIS

Desert Spadefoot Frog has red warning spots

FACTS

- The Sandhill Frog was the first Australian frog to be protected by law.
- The scientist who named the Sandhill Frog in 1976, Michael Tyler, was told in 1978 that he could not catch any for study because the species was endangered. However, this frog is now known to be quite common in its sandhill habitat.
- The Desert Spadefoot Frog spends dry periods underground. After heavy rain it emerges, sometimes in very large numbers. A dry road through the flooded desert may be crowded with tiny fat frogs trying to keep out of the water.

DID YOU KNOW?

FACTS

- Newly hatched narrow-mouthed frogs are so tiny that 20 of them would fit on a five-cent coin.
- Narrow-mouthed frogs stay in close contact with their eggs until the young frogs emerge. Perhaps antibacterial and antifungal secretions from the parent's skin protect the eggs.
- The newly hatched froglets of some New Guinea species of narrow-mouthed frogs cling to the male's back and are carried around for some time.
- Narrow-mouthed frogs live in moist tropical rainforest and their continued survival depends on the preservation of this habitat.
- India and Bangladesh have banned export of frogs for human consumption. One reason is the spectacular increase in insect pests in areas in which frogs have become rare.
- However, a number of South-East Asian countries continue to export frogs for human consumption.

NARROW-MOUTHED FROGS AND A TRUE FROG

Australia's other frogs

Many members of the family known as the narrow-mouthed frogs are found in South America, Madagascar and New Guinea.

Nearly all the Australian members of the family, such as Fry's Chirper (or Fry's Whistling Frog), occur in Cape York Peninsula, suggesting that their ancestors may have crossed a land bridge from New Guinea some time in the past, when sea levels were lower.

Narrow-mouthed frogs are small frogs which lay their eggs on land, in damp, quiet places such as under leaf litter. The egg clusters are guarded, usually by the male frog. The tadpole never leaves the egg capsule and eventually tiny, fully formed frogs hatch from the eggs.

Some frogs in this family have large discs on their fingers and are good climbers. However, they do not have the piece of cartilage between the final bones of the digits which marks the tree-frogs.

Fry's Chirper lives in north Queensland rainforest

Australia's "true frog"

Australia is home to only one member of the group known as the "true frogs", though in Europe, Asia and North America there are numbers of representatives of this group. (In other countries, "true frogs" have a long history of being eaten or used as laboratory animals.)

Australia's "true frog", the Australian Bullfrog, reached the continent from New Guinea. It is found on Cape York Peninsula, Queensland, and in Arnhem Land, Northern Territory. Usually seen at night, in grass near permanent water, it has fully-webbed toes, is a powerful swimmer and has a fold of skin running from eye to hind limb on each side of its body. A male of this species has a two-lobed vocal sac.

The Australian Bullfrog makes a ducklike, quacking call

An ill-fated importation

Though 206 species of toad exist worldwide, the introduced Cane Toad is Australia's only true toad.

The Cane Toad is native to northern South America and Central America north to Texas, USA. This includes areas of seasonal drought as well as tropical areas, and the toad is able to adapt to conditions other frogs find difficult. It had been introduced into at least 14 countries to control insect pests when it was released in Australia in 1935 as a biological control on beetles in the canefields of northeastern Queensland. (When the Cane Toad was introduced to Australia, insecticides were not available. The only way of controlling beetles was to collect them by hand.) However, the toad gobbled anything it could catch and multiplied, often at the expense of native frogs. It has now spread south into New South Wales and north and west to the Gulf country of Queensland and the Northern Territory.

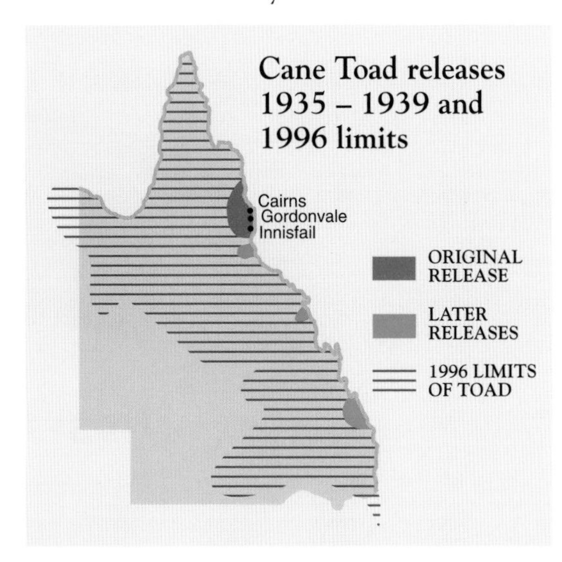

PURE POISON

The egg, tadpole and adult of the Cane Toad are poisonous to animals which mouth or eat them. The adult Cane Toad has large glands on its shoulders which contain a milky toxin. If the toad is provoked, the fluid can be squirted for up to one metre. Many Australian animals eat frogs. Just one bite at a Cane Toad can cause death. A few predators, such as crows, learn to turn the toad over and peck at its belly. Purple Swamphens attack toads through their mouths, pulling out their insides. A very few, for example the Keelback Snake, appear immune to the toxin.*

The Cane Toad has colonised most of northeastern Australia since it was introduced in 1935

FACTS

- The largest Cane Toad on record in Australia measured just over 24 cm in length, was 16.5 cm wide and weighed 1.36 kg.
- A Cane Toad can survive dehydration which reduces its body weight by half. It replaces its body fluids when water becomes available.
- The Cane Toad's call is a purring similar to a telephone dial tone.
- A captive Cane Toad lived to 16 years.
- The original, 1935 importation of Cane Toads consisted of 102 animals. They bred, and 3400 young toads were released around Cairns, Gordonvale and Innisfail. Other releases were made in 1939.
- Beekeepers have to raise their hives over half a metre from the ground on stands because Cane Toads gather around hives and gulp down bees.
- The Queensland Government's wedding gift to Prince Charles and Princess Diana was a book bound in Cane Toad skin.

What is happening to frogs?

Frogs are vanishing from the world

A World Congress held in England in 1989 was told that a serious decline of many frog species seems to have begun between 1978 and 1983. It continues, and some frogs may be extinct.

"Acid rain", tainted by wastes from burning coal and oil, pollution of waterways by salt, pesticides and other chemicals, habitat loss because of drainage of swamps and clearing of forests, global warming, and increasing ultraviolet radiation due to the thinning of the protective ozone layer of the atmosphere – all may share responsibility. Australian frogs are not taken for human food, but have to contend with introduced predators and competitors such as the Cane Toad.

At present, at least 34 species of Australia's frogs should be considered "endangered" or "vulnerable". Little is known about many of these frogs and there is not enough known about another 30 species to decide whether they are endangered or not.

Since the early 1970s, seven species of frogs, including the two gastric-brooding frogs, have apparently disappeared from mountain streams between Brisbane and Cairns. Another seven species have become rare. The cause of this may be a frog-specific virus, transmitted in some way that affects frogs living at altitudes above 300 metres.

The Australian National Conservation Agency has initiated a plan to identify frog species requiring conservation. There are also studies being made of the declining frogs of New South Wales and Queensland.

IAN MORRIS

Red-eyed Tree-frog

Australian Bullfrog

Frogs monitor the environment

Frogs are extremely sensitive to changes in the environment.

Exposure of developing eggs to harmful substances may kill them, or may result in the adult frogs which come from them having deformed, additional, or missing digits or limbs, or other abnormalities. Some species' eggs are very sensitive to increased levels of ultraviolet radiation and even small amounts may prevent them hatching.

The decline of frogs may indicate deterioration in air, soil, surface water and rainfall quality a long time before humans are aware of pollution by salt, agricultural chemicals and industrial wastes.

As frog expert Michael J. Tyler wrote in his entertaining and informative book *Australian Frogs:*

"... the innocent frog is being appreciated as a sensitive indicator organism of subtle environmental change. It constitutes an early, environmental warning system of benefit to humanity."

How to help your local frogs survive

- Learn as much as you can about frogs in general and find out which frogs occur in your area.
- If developing land, do your best to preserve frog habitat. Don't drain frog-breeding sites.
- Make your garden frog-friendly, with damp, shady places. A backyard pond will attract frogs.
- Why not raise suitable frogs for your area? Stock your pond with locally caught tadpoles – don't introduce strangers from other areas.
- Remember that for frogs to exist tadpoles need to be left in peace.
- Don't use pesticides or herbicides if there is any other way of controlling a pest animal or plant.
- Discourage domestic pets from damaging or killing frogs.
- Learn to recognise Cane Toads (eggs are in strings not masses, tadpoles are completely black). Exterminate them from your garden.
- Don't eat frog legs.
- If you drive an off-road vehicle, avoid damaging creek banks, sand dunes and shallow swamps.
- Be sympathetic when your local frogs burst into song. Think of the noisy chorus as passionate love-songs and try to identify the species.

JIRI LOCHMAN

Frogs usually sing their love-songs most loudly at night

Emerald-spotted Tree-frog

STANLEY BREEDEN

White-lipped Tree-frog

What is a reptile?

A reptile is a vertebrate which, like amphibians, is ectothermic, its body temperature influenced by the temperature of its surroundings. Its body is covered with dry skin, from which grow scales.

The Saltwater Crocodile is an armoured, water-dwelling predator

Body wastes, eggs and sperm all leave the body of a reptile through the final section of the gut, which is called the cloaca*. A reptile's kidneys can change body wastes from liquid to solid form. Land reptiles' urine forms part of the limey waste material passed out of their bodies, but aquatic reptiles usually pass fluid urine as well as solid wastes.

The sperm produced by a male reptile fertilises a female's eggs inside her body (in amphibians, fertilisation takes place outside the body). The fertilised eggs of most reptile species are enclosed in shells and are laid on land. However, some species retain their eggs within their bodies until the young hatch.

Most reptiles eat other animals, though a few eat plant material.

Most reptiles have four limbs. Snakes have no limbs (though pythons have remnants), and some lizards have reduced limbs, only two hindlimbs, or scaly flaps instead of hindlimbs.

The four groups of reptiles

There are four groups of reptiles alive today. Members of three groups are found in Australia. The three groups are:

- **turtles**
- **crocodilians**
- **lizards and snakes**

The sole member of the fourth group, the **Tuatara,** is found only in New Zealand.

Lungs and hearts

When it breathes, a reptile expands its ribs, drawing air into its lungs. After oxygen and carbon dioxide have been exchanged in the lungs, the reptile breathes out by contracting its ribs. In a few water-living species, some exchange of gases takes place through the skin or even the cloaca.

Turtles, lizards and snakes have three-chambered hearts. In the single lower chamber, oxygenated blood coming from the lungs may mix with deoxygenated blood from the body.

Crocodiles have four-chambered hearts, like those of birds and mammals. Normally oxygenated and deoxygenated blood do not mix, but during a long dive, when fresh air is not available, a special valve allows deoxygenated blood to pass back into the crocodile's body tissues.

On a miniature scale, the Marbled Velvet Gecko is as deadly a predator as a crocodile MARIE LOCHMAN

JIRI LOCHMAN

The Western Swamp Turtle, Australia's most endangered reptile, aestivates during summer drought periods

Desert survivors

Australia's many dry areas are full of reptiles which are adapted to arid conditions in a number of ways:

- Their body wastes have very little water in them.
- They obtain water from their food, and from licking dew. The scales of some lizards channel water to the mouth.
- Because of their low energy requirements, reptiles can survive food scarcities during drought.
- Small reptiles feed on ants and termites, which are plentiful in the desert. The small reptiles are then eaten by larger reptiles.
- A reptile becomes active when the temperature is right for its species. In the desert, it may forage at night, and shelter in a burrow during the day, or spend daytime shuttling from sunshine to shade and back again. Some lizards climb some distance off the ground into vegetation to avoid ground heat.

The Frilled Lizard, a northern predator

Wetlands predators

The floodplains of northern Australia support a greater weight of predators in a given area than do Africa's Serengeti Plains.

The African predators are mammals such as lions and hyenas. The Australian ones are reptiles, such as water-living pythons, file snakes, freshwater turtles, crocodiles and a variety of lizards, including the Frilled Lizard. These creatures eat each other, as well as insects and other invertebrates, fish, frogs and small mammals.

FACTS

- Worldwide, there are about 6400 living species of reptiles.
- Snakes and lizards make up nearly 95% of living reptile species.
- Around 700 species of reptiles are found in Australia. There are more species in the warmer north than in the cooler south.
- Few reptiles can survive exposure to temperatures over 50°C.
- Reptiles living in cool climates become torpid* or hibernate* when the weather becomes too cold.
- Reptiles from cool climates may become active at around 20°C. Those from hot deserts need to warm up to around 35°C before becoming active.
- A reptile continues to grow throughout its lifetime, but the rate of growth slows as it ages.
- The embryos of a few reptile species are not enclosed in eggshells. They develop within their mothers' bodies, their bloodstreams linked to their mothers' by placentas* like those found in placental mammals.
- A person who studies reptiles is called a herpetologist*.

The history of Australia's reptiles

What fossils reveal

25 000+ YEARS AGO

Reptiles at Riversleigh, in western Queensland, included giant crocodiles, giant turtles, monitor lizards and pythons.

100 000+ YEARS AGO

The Wellington Caves area of NSW was home to a flesh-eating goanna called *Megalania.* It grew to about 6 m in length, was a ferocious predator and may have existed as recently as 30 000 years ago.

15 MILLION+ YEARS AGO

The Riversleigh reptiles included a large horned turtle with a clubbed tail, giant pythons, crocodiles and a water dragon lizard.

110 MILLION+ YEARS AGO

Crocodilians lived at Lightning Ridge, NSW.

135-65 MILLION YEARS AGO

Muttaburrasaurus, a plant-eating dinosaur about 7 m in length, lived in Queensland.

145-65 MILLION YEARS AGO

An inland sea covered central Australia. In it swam ichthyosaurs and the 15-metres-long pliosaur *Kronosaurus.* Dinosaur Cove, Victoria, was home to the huge flesh-eater *Allosaurus.*

210-145 MILLION YEARS AGO

A plant-eating dinosaur, *Rhoetosaurus,* more than 15 m long and weighing 20 tonnes, lived at Taloona Station, near Roma, Queensland.

245-210 MILLION YEARS AGO

The early reptile *Tasmaniosaurus* hunted amphibians near Old Beach, Tasmania.

Reptiles developed from amphibians. Their distant ancestors developed characteristics which allowed them to survive on land and to reproduce without returning to the water.

By about 250 million years ago reptiles were common on land and in salt and fresh water. They became the dominant vertebrate group, reaching their peak about 145-65 million years ago. At that time, Australia was joined to other continents and lay far south of where it is today. It was home to dinosaurs, flying pterosaurs and swimming ichthyosaurs, as well as to other sorts of reptiles. By 65 million years ago, the dinosaurs had become extinct (though their descendants, birds, are still with us), while turtles, crocodilians, snakes and lizards survived.

By about 50 million years ago, Australia had separated from Antarctica and was drifting slowly northwards. Until 25 million years ago, much of the continent was covered by rainforest. Since then, the landmass has become much drier. Some reptiles remained in the dwindling rainforest, others adapted to living in more arid conditions.

Relatively recently, when sea levels were lower, some lizards and snakes migrated over a land bridge from New Guinea to Cape York.

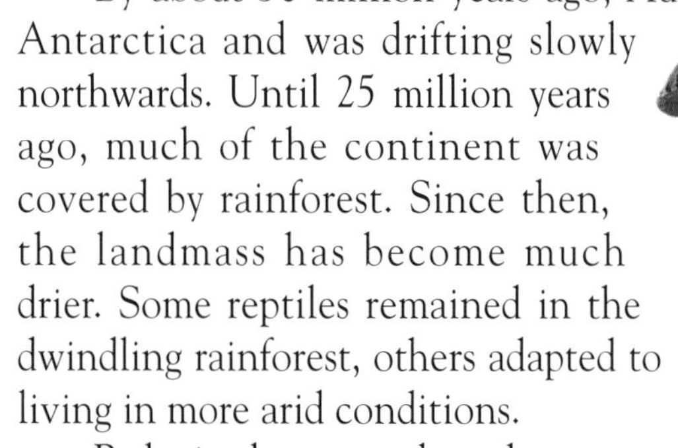

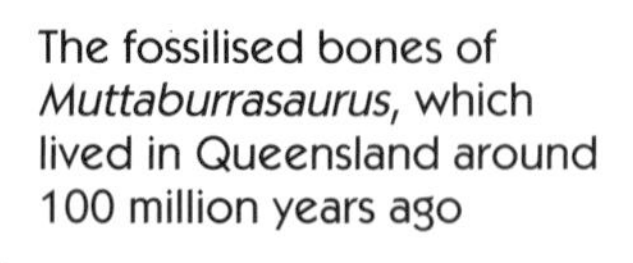

The fossilised bones of *Muttaburrasaurus*, which lived in Queensland around 100 million years ago

QUEENSLAND MUSEUM

Australia's largest modern snake, the Amethyst Python. Giant fossil snakes, seven metres in length, have been discovered at Riversleigh, Queensland, and other sites

What is a fossil?

A fossil is the trace of a plant or animal which lived some time in the past. It may have been preserved whole (e.g. an insect in amber), or as an imprint (e.g. dinosaur tracks in rock). Soft tissues or bones may have been replaced by a harder, substance such as stone. Some fossils can be dated by measuring the amount by which radioactive* substances, deposited in, or near, them in the same era, have decayed since they were formed.

JIRI LOCHMAN

The Thorny Devil is well adapted to life in the arid areas which today dominate Australia's centre

FACTS
ABOUT A MODERN REPTILE DISCOVERY

Two hundred years after Europeans began cataloguing Australia's reptiles, new species continue to be added to the list.

One of the latest is the Mary River Turtle. In 1961, John Cann, an amateur herpetologist, began seeing mystery baby turtles, with shells the size of a 50 cent piece, on sale in pet shops. In the mid-1970s it became illegal to sell tiny turtles and no more "pet-shop turtles" were seen.

In the early 1980s, a large "pet-shop turtle", with a shell the size of a saucer, was found dumped in a drain in Centennial Park, in the heart of Sydney, NSW.

John continued to track down the mystery turtle. He decided it came from the Mary River, in southern Queensland.

In 1990, John searched the Mary River and eventually spotted a dinner-plate-sized turtle sitting on a rock. He had found the Mary River Turtle in its natural habitat. Adult males of this species have the longest tails of any known turtle (up to 70% of the turtle's shell length).

Unfortunately, the Mary River is becoming increasingly polluted by agricultural run-off and debris from sand-mining.

DID YOU KNOW?

FACTS

- There is neither a skin nor a skeleton of an Australian Saltwater Crocodile over 6.7 metres in length.
- Most of a crocodile's strenuous activity is anaerobic*. Afterwards the crocodile must rest, so it can repay its oxygen debt* and get rid of acid waste products from its body.
- A large crocodile struggles violently when captured and may die because it cannot pay back its oxygen debt.
- "Sweetheart", whose remains are now in the Darwin Museum, was just over 5 m long and weighed 780 kg. He was caught after attacking several fishing dinghies, probably irritated by the roar of their outboard motors, but died soon after capture.

Armoured predators

The crocodilian group includes crocodiles, alligators, caimans and gharials. Australia is home to two of the 22 living species of crocodiles, but has no other crocodilians.

Australian Freshwater Crocodile

A crocodile is superbly adapted to its lifestyle as an aquatic predator. While each of its sturdy front limbs has five unwebbed fingers, each hindlimb has five toes, three of which are webbed and clawed. It swims by moving its tail from side to side.

Its head is covered by bony plates overlaid by thick skin. The eyes, ears and nostrils are on the top of the head and remain above water while the rest of the body is submerged. A crocodile can breathe through its mouth or through its nostrils, and inhales air by moving its internal organs backwards, so the lungs expand.

The jaws gape widely and close with tremendous force. The conical teeth mesh to secure prey and if a tooth is lost a replacement waits underneath. A flap of skin at the back of the throat stops water entering the gullet when the crocodile opens its mouth underwater. Crocodiles are the only reptiles whose hearts have four chambers. When a crocodile dives, a shunt* acts to channel its blood flow so that while the brain continues to receive oxygenated blood the other organs receive deoxygenated blood.

A crocodile's skin is covered by a network of scales, which are flat on the belly, but raised on the sides and the back. Extra "armour-plating" protection is given by bony lumps called osteoderms*, which are embedded in the skin.

Crocodile or alligator?

A crocodile's large lower canine teeth are still visible when the owner's mouth is closed. An alligator's canine teeth fit into sockets in the upper jaw, so are invisible when the mouth is closed. There are no alligators in Australia, only crocodiles.

PETER SLATER

Modern relatives of the dinosaurs, a bird and a crocodile

When a crocodile's mouth is closed, its lower canine tooth can still be seen

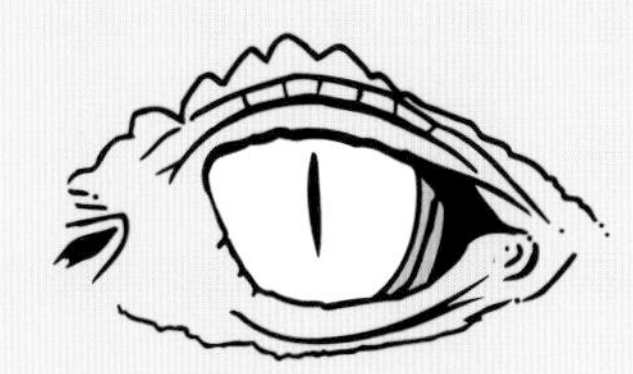

Above water

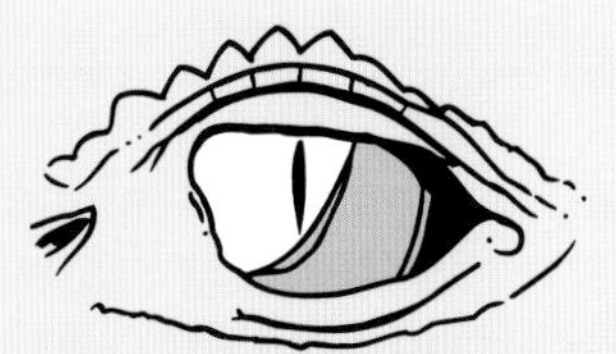

As the crocodile submerges

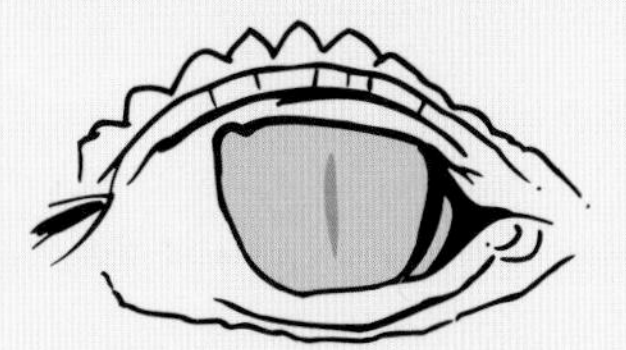

... see-through third eyelid slides across the eye

PAT SLATER

Saltwater Crocodile floating, eyes and nostrils above water

PAT SLATER

Underwater, nostrils closed and "third eyelid" across the eye

"Salties"

The broad-snouted, stout-toothed Saltwater, or Estuarine, Crocodile occurs across northern Australia. It lives in fresh, salt and brackish water, especially in rivers crossing coastal flood plains.

An adult male may reach between five and six metres in length, with an occasional individual reaching nearly seven metres. Heavily hunted in the past, today this crocodile is farmed for its skin and flesh. It is known to attack humans and other large animals and is regarded as dangerous.

... and "Freshies"

The narrow-snouted, needle-toothed Freshwater Crocodile of northern Australia rarely exceeds three metres in length. It is seldom found in tidal areas and inhabits rivers, billabongs and swamps.

During the Wet season, these crocodiles travel with the floodwaters, but for the Dry they return to permanent water. The Freshwater Crocodile eats fish and small aquatic animals such as crabs and prawns. It does not view humans as prey,

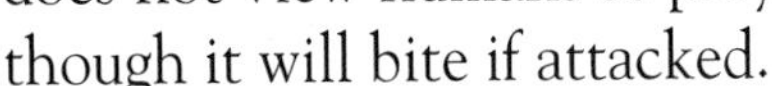

though it will bite if attacked.

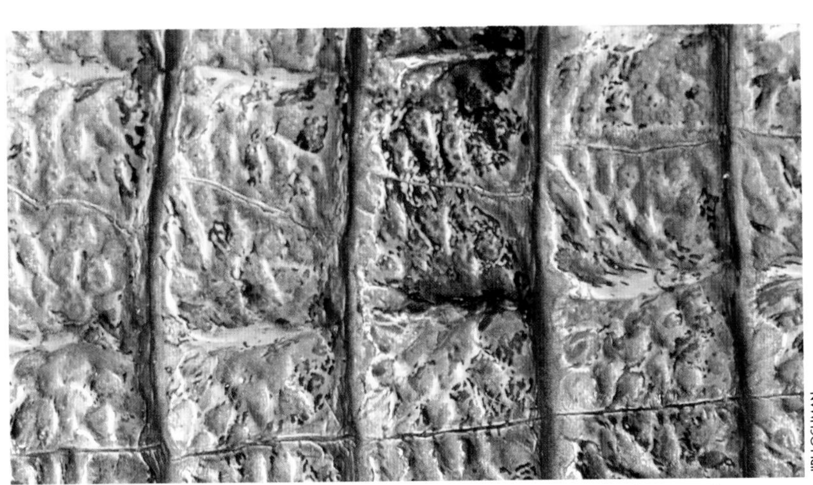

JIRI LOCHMAN

Each scale on the back of a crocodile contains a bony, raised osteoderm

BELINDA WRIGHT

Saltwater Crocodile swallowing a Barramundi

FACTS

- A crocodile has 66 teeth, each of which may be replaced many times over the owner's lifespan.
- The muscles which close a crocodile's jaws are immensely powerful. Even if a victim survives the attack, the flesh around the tooth-wounds is "killed", leading to infection.
- The muscles which open a crocodile's jaws are relatively weak.
- A crocodile's tail carries two rows of raised boneless scales or scutes*. These contain blood vessels and when exposed to heat help warm the crocodile's body. The scutes also increase the "paddle" area of the tail.

DID YOU KNOW?

FACTS ABOUT CROCODILE SOCIETY

- A crocodile threatened by another crocodile will raise its snout out of the water to show submission.
- Freshwater Crocodiles may become very crowded together in small pools during the Dry season. A large male will dominate a group by biting the tails of other adults.
- As the breeding season approaches, large male Saltwater Crocodiles patrol stretches of water, challenging approaching crocodiles. Rival males will growl, slap their heads on the water and sometimes fight.
- Saltwater Crocodiles may be seen with parts of limbs or tails missing due to attacks by other crocodiles.

How crocodiles live and behave

A crocodile receives information from its surroundings in a number of ways which allow it to locate prey and to evade danger.

It has good hearing, can hear both high-pitched and low-pitched sounds and can pinpoint the location of potential prey by sound alone.

The forward placement of the eyes on the head and the short distance between them give binocular vision like that of a human. This allows accurate estimation of distances when hunting. Like the eye of a cat, each eye contains a reflecting layer of crystals which intensifies vision in low light and the vertical pupil opens to a circle in low light and closes to a slit in strong light. The sense of smell is keen. The brain contains large areas which receive and analyse odours. Along the sides of a crocodile's jaws are pits sensitive to touch and vibration.

Crocodiles spend much of their time in activities which regulate the temperature of their bodies. They bask in the sun, shelter amongst vegetation, or lie in shallow water or in a mud wallow.

A male crocodile may hold a territory on a stretch of water and challenge intruding crocodiles. During the breeding season, he will mate with a number of females. A female will build or excavate a nest, lay her eggs in it, then stay near it. When the young call from within the eggs, the female excavates the nest and carries the hatchlings to the water in her mouth.

Snap!

Both species of crocodile take prey by lying in ambush, then snapping sideways at animals in the water or on the bank.

Another method used is to locate prey, then swim to it underwater, lunge, grab it and drag it into the water. The lunge, powered by the tail, may take the crocodile half its body length up the bank or into the air. The crocodile "death-rolls" and twists the prey under water until it is subdued. Pieces may then be torn off and swallowed. A crocodile has a comparatively small stomach (a three-metre crocodile has a stomach about the size of a basketball) and a large carcass may be "stored" for future consumption under a submerged log or undercut bank.

PAT SLATER

A crocodile can lunge half out of the water by lashing its powerful tail

A Freshwater Crocodile can sprint briefly at 18 km/h

BELINDA WRIGHT

A basking crocodile absorbs heat through its body scales. It opens its mouth so its brain remains cool

Temperature decides the sex of baby crocodiles

The temperature at which crocodile eggs are kept while the young they contain are developing determines the sex of the youngsters. Incubation* at 30ºC or less produces females, incubation around 31ºC produces both sexes, and incubation between 32ºC and 33ºC produces exclusively males.

During the northern Wet season, a female Saltwater Crocodile makes a nest of vegetation close to the water. Four to six weeks after mating, she lays up to 60 eggs in it, then remains close to the nest. She may roll hatching eggs in her mouth, squeezing them until the young emerge. She carries them to the water in her mouth and then remains with them for some months.

In the Dry season, a female Australian Freshwater Crocodile lays about 12 eggs in a nest dug into sand. Several females may nest close together. When the young hatch, the female carries them to the water (her sharp teeth sometimes damage them), then stays with them.

SALTWATER CROCODILE SURVIVAL TO FIVE YEARS OLD

Eggs	1000
Hatchlings	250
Survive to 1 year	135
Survive to 2 years	41
Survive to 3 years	24
Survive to 4 years	14
Survive to 5 years	8

MARIE LOCHMAN

A newly hatched Saltwater Crocodile

FACTS

- Courting Saltwater Crocodiles swim around each other, rubbing heads and bodies together. Mating takes place underwater, with the male on the female's back, twisting his tail under hers until their vents make contact.
- Stones found in crocodiles' stomachs may help grind food. They may also serve as ballast*, allowing the crocodile to maintain a position underwater with little effort.
- Most attacks on humans by wild Saltwater Crocodiles are made on swimmers (particularly at night), canoeists and people bending down in shallow water.
- A Saltwater Crocodile nest may be 80 cm high and is made of vegetation broken off by the female's teeth, or scraped up with he clawed hindfeet.

Saltwater Crocodile nest

DID YOU KNOW?

FACTS

- Worldwide, there are about 210 living species of tortoises and turtles.
- Only 7 species of marine turtles exist today. Six of the 7 occur in Australian waters. Five of the 7 are endangered.
- Around 23 species of freshwater turtles occur in Australia.
- Around 200 million years ago, the ancestors of turtles lived on land. The form of sea turtles has changed little in the past 100 million years.
- Roman legionaries used to form a "tortoise" by closing ranks and holding their shields over their heads. The "shell" protected them from missiles.

Between shells

The Pig-nosed Turtle is a freshwater turtle with flippers like those of a sea turtle

Turtles live in or near water and their legs end in flippers or webbed feet. Tortoises live on land and their stumpy legs end in unwebbed feet. Both have horny cutting edges on their jaws instead of teeth. The two groups are closely related, but there are no Australian tortoises and any four-limbed, shelled animal seen here, in or near either fresh or salt water, is a turtle.

A turtle or tortoise has its body enclosed in a shell made up of a carapace* on top and a plastron* below, joined at the sides. The carapace is usually fused to the turtle's ribs and backbone. Carapace and plastron are made up of bony plates, usually covered with horny shields.

The turtle's head and forelimbs protrude through a gap at the front of its shell, while the tail and hindlimbs poke through a gap at the rear. Some species can withdraw the head between the halves of the shell, or tuck it under the front edge of the carapace. Others must leave the head exposed and vulnerable.

A marine turtle's flippers are vulnerable to predators. When attacked, these turtles have been seen to float at the surface, flippers raised.

Necks that S-bend

Australia's freshwater and marine turtles can be divided into two groups according to the ways in which they bend their necks.

The seven species of marine turtles and the freshwater Pig-nosed Turtles flex their necks by bending them into vertical S-shapes. None of these species can fully pull the head back under the shell.

The rest of the Australian turtles, all of which are found in fresh water, bend their necks into horizontal S-shapes. They may have long or short necks; some are able to pull in their heads as well as withdraw their tails.

An Eastern Snake-necked Turtle pulls its head in for protection

BELINDA WRIGHT

A freshwater turtle displays its webbed toe and horizontal S-bend neck

A young Gagudju (NT) hunter and his long-necked catch

STANLEY BREEDEN

Freshwater turtles have long provided food sources for the Aboriginal people. These turtles are taken from the water, or dug up from the burrows in which they aestivate when seasonal wetlands dry up. In this case, the body fat which provides the turtle with energy reserves during its imprisonment makes it particularly valued prey.

Rock painting of a long-necked turtle

STANLEY BREEDEN

A turtle's upper shell is called the carapace

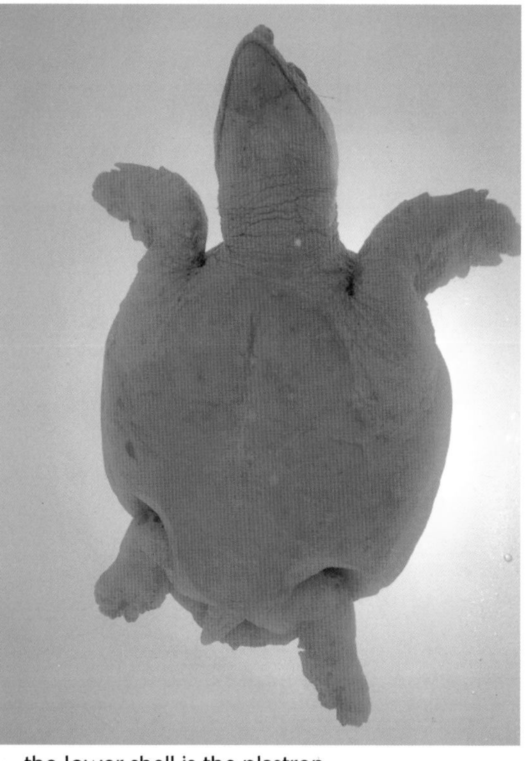

... the lower shell is the plastron

FACTS

- The shell is the primary defence for a turtle, but some species of freshwater turtles have glands in the groin and sometimes in the armpit. These release unpleasant-smelling fluid to deter predators.
- In time of drought, freshwater turtles may trek overland to find new water, or else bury themselves to wait for rainfall.
- Turtles mate in the water. A male will follow a female, circling her and attempting to climb onto her from behind. If she responds, he mounts and clings on to her shell with his front feet. Then he lowers his shell until he can twist his tail under hers and their vents meet.
- Marine turtles may have flippers mutilated by sharks, or by becoming entangled in fishing gear or plastic debris.
- Humans take adult marine turtles and their eggs for food. Many turtles drown in nets set to catch fish.

DID YOU KNOW?

FACTS

- A turtle rows itself through the water with its front flippers and steers with its rear flippers.
- A male sea turtle has claws on his front flippers. These hold the female while mating.
- Hatchling turtles usually emerge at night. Light attracts them, delaying their rush to the ocean and making them even more vulnerable to attack by predators.
- Soon after hatching, tiny turtles drift with the ocean currents, feeding on minute marine animals. They are rarely seen again until their shell length is 35-40 cm, which may be five or ten years after hatching.

Rare, vanishing seafarers

The Olive Ridley is the smallest turtle in Australian waters

The forelimbs of a marine turtle are paddle-like flippers. The shell is low-domed, streamlined and comparatively light, giving maximum protection while allowing the turtle to be buoyant and to move easily through the water. These turtles get their water requirements from seawater and excess salt is excreted from glands next to their eyes.

Sea turtles are much bigger than freshwater turtles. The largest species, the giant Leatherback, can grow to two metres in length and may weigh as much as 960 kilograms. The smallest sea turtle, the Olive Ridley, grows to 75 centimetres in length and weighs up to 40 kilograms.

The Loggerhead, Flatback, Green and Hawksbill Turtles regularly nest along the Queensland coast. Leatherback Turtles nest from time to time on Queensland and Arnhem coasts, while Olive Ridleys nest around the Gulf of Carpentaria and on Arnhem Land beaches and islands.

Mate at sea, lay on land

During the breeding season, sea turtles migrate to mating areas near nesting beaches. They mate with a number of partners and the females store sperm in their bodies to fertilise the multiple batches of eggs they will lay during the season.

To lay, a female turtle drags herself up the beach to a nest site with her front flippers, which are then used to excavate a body pit. The egg chamber is scooped out by the back flippers, working alternately. After laying, the back flippers fill the chamber, then she hauls herself down to the sea again. She will lay several clutches at two-weekly intervals.

The sex of the hatchlings depends on the nest temperature during incubation. The babies take about 24 hours to get out of their eggshells; they are vulnerable to predators on the beach and in the water.

Turtle laying eggs in egg chamber

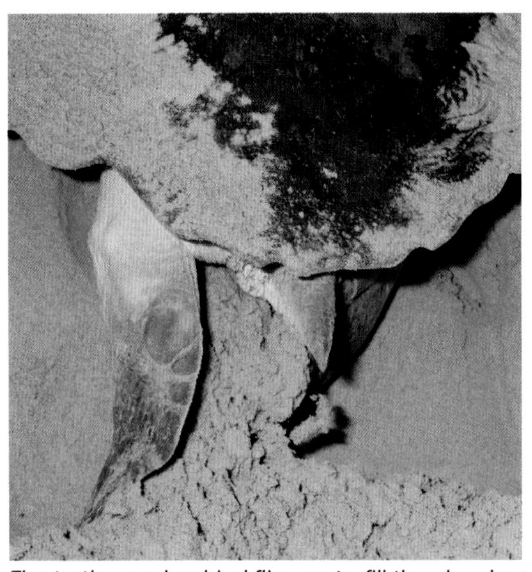

The turtle uses her hind flippers to fill the chamber

A Green Turtle hatchling

The Flatback Turtle is found only in Australian waters

The Hawksbill Turtle is an endangered species

Turtle menus

The horny jaws of each species of sea turtle are adapted to obtaining its favoured foods.

The Green Turtle eats seaweed and seagrasses (and its tasty flesh is eaten by humans). The Hawksbill Turtle's pointed jaws prise molluscs, sponges, shellfish and algae from coral crevices. The small Olive Ridley eats crustaceans, sea urchins, sea jellies and algae. The Loggerhead Turtle's powerful jaw muscles enable it to feed on shellfish, crabs and sea urchins. The Leatherback, with its notched jaws, feeds on sea jellies.

The large-skulled Loggerhead Turtle

The record-breaking Leatherback

The Leatherback is the largest turtle. It may be unique amongst reptiles, for it seems to produce body heat internally, by breaking down special fat deposits in its body. Its internal temperature may be up to 18°C higher than the temperature of the surrounding water.

The Leatherback's light, streamlined, leathery shell contains many small bones (osteoderms) embedded in rubbery skin. Leatherbacks swim great distances from their tropical breeding grounds to cool temperate feeding grounds and may dive to 1000 metres or more, staying submerged for more than 30 minutes. They may die after eating floating plastic bags, which they mistake for sea jellies.

FACTS

- Sea turtles may be between 30 and 50 years old before the[y] breed. A Green Turtl[e] may be 48 years of a[ge] before it breeds.
- The Loggerhead Turt[les] nesting each summe[r] near Bundaberg, Qld, are genetically different from those nesting in other parts of the world.
- The Hawksbill Turtle's survival is threatened by the "tortoiseshell" trade.
- The Flatback Turtle is found only in Australian waters. Its flattened shell has upturned edges and [is] covered by skin. It e[ats] soft corals, cuttles a[nd] jellyfish. The Flatback nests around northe[rn] Australia; the large hatchlings are about 6 cm long.

This Green Turtle's tears are excreting excess salt

The Leatherback is the world's largest turtle

Waiting for rain

Saw-shelled Turtle

Australia has around six species of snake-necked (long-necked) freshwater turtles and ten species of short-necked turtles.

Some species of Australian freshwater turtles live in permanent water, others have to contend with regular seasonal dry conditions and occasional droughts. Freshwater turtles leave the water to bask in the sun, lay their eggs and sometimes to travel overland to other bodies of water if their home dries up. They respond to extremely cold conditions, and also to extreme heat or drought, by remaining inactive underground.

Freshwater turtles are mainly carnivorous, taking fish, molluscs, frogs, insects and small waterbirds. Some species may eat vegetation, such as fallen fruit, and occasionally carrion.

Australia's rarest reptile

The most endangered of all Australia's reptiles is the short-necked Western Swamp Turtle. It has a wild population of around 20 living in one swamp at Ellenbrook, near Perth, Western Australia.

These turtles spend up to nine months of each year aestivating and are active only for a few months after winter rains flood their habitat. Hatchlings need two years' growth before they have enough body mass to cope with a drought season.

DID YOU KNOW?

FACTS ABOUT SHORT-NECKED FRESHWATER TURTLES

- The Murray Short-necked Turtle lives at the highest altitude known for any Australian freshwater turtle, about 1000 m above sea level, on the New England Tableland, NSW.
- Some short-necked turtles develop huge heads with powerful jaw muscles, possibly as a response to cracking the shells of mussels. This macrocephalic* condition is nicknamed "boof-headedness".
- The Saw-shelled Turtle is one of the few animals which has been seen to eat Cane Toads with no observed ill effects. Large toads were shredded with the front claws before being swallowed.

Eastern Snake-necked Turtle

The bumps on the neck of the endangered Western Swamp Turtle are touch-sensitive

JIRI LOCHMAN

The Northern Snake-necked Turtle has a large head

IAN MORRIS

Northern Short-necked Turtle eating fallen figs

The Pig-nosed Turtle has a shell covered with skin

Broad-shelled Snake-necked Turtle in ambush

The Warrajan

The remarkable Pig-nosed Turtle, or Warrajan, has a fleshy snout with nostrils at its end. Its bony shell is covered with soft, pitted skin. This freshwater turtle rows itself through the water like a sea turtle, using scaleless, paddle-shaped flippers, each with two claws.

The Pig-nosed Turtle was first discovered in Australia in 1969, in the Daly River, Northern Territory, and has been found in the Alligator and Victoria Rivers as well. It feeds on snails, fish and fruit. The female Pig-nose lays around 15 parchment-shelled eggs on a sandbank or mudbank in the late Dry season. The embryos develop, but remain "asleep" until the nest is flooded after the Wet begins. Then they hatch at night and rush into the water.

A peculiar way of breathing

The Fitzroy Turtle, which lives in fast-flowing rivers in central coastal Queensland, rarely needs to surface to breathe.

Between 15 and 60 times per minute, it pumps water in and out of its cloaca, the final section of its gut. Here pouches lined with blood-vessels act as gills to take oxygen from the water.

JIRI LOCHMAN

This Kimberley turtle is a recent discovery and has no common name

FACTS
ABOUT SNAKE-NECKED FRESHWATER TURTLES

- The head and neck of a snake-necked turtle are together as long as, or longer than, the carapace.
- Snake-necked turtles have only four claws on the webbed front feet. Other species of Australian freshwater turtles have five.
- A hunting turtle approaches prey with its neck held sideways near the shell, then lunges its neck forward and opens its mouth, sucking in water and prey together.
- A snake-necked turtle may conceal itself by paddling mud or debris over its shell as it lies on the bottom. From time to time, the neck is poked up to the surface so the turtle can breathe.
- Snake-necked turtles have scent glands in groins and sometimes armpits.

DID YOU KNOW?

FACTS

- Worldwide, there are about 3000 living species of lizards.
- The number of lizard species in Australia is constantly being revised. Species new to science are being added to the list. Species already named may be "split" into two or more as scientists discover more about them.
- Skinks, legless lizards and geckos may grow a new tail if the original is shed. The new tail is supported by a rod of cartilage, not by vertebrae*. It may be shorter, and is a different colour from the original.
- Although only monitors have deeply forked tongues, the fleshy tongues of other Australian lizards have notches at their tips.

Five fascinating families

STANLEY BREEDEN

Ring-tailed Bicycle-dragon

Lizards and snakes belong to the same major group of reptiles, the Squamata or "scaled reptiles". They have similarities and differences (see also p. 43).

- **The scales** which cover the bodies of lizards and snakes are embedded in their skins and protected by a thin, horny outer layer, which is shed at intervals.
- **The teeth** of lizards and snakes are fused to the edges of their upper and lower jaws. In some groups of snakes, some of these teeth deliver venom when biting. No Australian lizard is venomous.
- **Four limbs** are present in most lizards, though some lizards have reduced limbs, only two limbs or no limbs at all. Snakes have no limbs, though a python has the remnants of a leg on either side of its vent.
- **Male lizards and snakes** have two hemipenes*, or paired penises, which lie in cavities at the base of the tail and are pushed out of the vent for mating.
- **The tails** of some sorts of lizards can be shed to distract predators. The tail breaks away at a fracture point and may or may not regrow. Snakes cannot shed their tails.

JIRI LOCHMAN

The Lowlands Earless Skink has no earhole. Its legs are very reduced

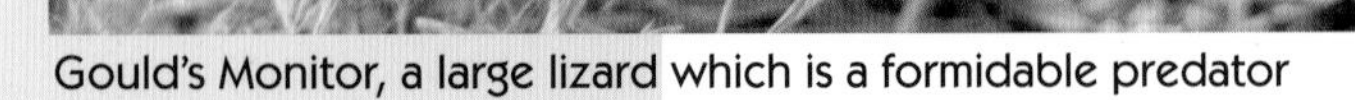

IAN MORRIS

Gould's Monitor, a large lizard which is a formidable predator

JIRI LOCHMAN

Fraser's Delma is a lizard with no legs and a fleshy, notched tongue

A Three-lined Knob-tailed Gecko cleaning its eye. It has an obvious earhole and sturdy legs

JIRI LOCHMAN

The five families of Australian lizards

GECKOS are soft-skinned, usually nocturnal* lizards with five well developed fingers and toes ending in pads or claws. Their eyes have vertical pupils and are covered by transparent lower lids fused to the upper lids. The tail may be shed and regrow. There are about 100 Australian species.

LEGLESS LIZARDS are snake-like lizards with overlapping scales. They have no forelimbs and the hind limbs are represented by flaps on either side of the vent. Their eyelids are fused and transparent. Part of the tail may be shed and regrow. Australia contains over 30 species.

DRAGONS are day-active lizards whose head scales and upper body scales often end in points and may form crests. They have well-developed limbs and are good runners and climbers. Their eyes have round pupils and movable eyelids. Dragons' tails cannot be shed. There are over 60 Australian species.

MONITORS (sometimes known as goannas) are active daytime hunters, with small scales which do not overlap. They have strong, well developed limbs and tails. The tongue is long and forked and is constantly flicked in and out of the mouth. The eye has a round pupil. The tail is not shed. There are about 25 Australian species.

SKINKS are usually daytime hunters, but a few species are nocturnal. The scales are usually smooth and overlapping and in burrowing species are very glossy. The limbs may be well developed, or reduced in size or number, or missing. The tongue is broad, flat and fleshy. Some species have movable eyelids, others have transparent lower lids fused to the upper lids. A shed tail will regenerate. There are over 300 Australian species.

FACTS

- Legless lizards and geckos, which have fixed eyelids, use their tongues to clean their eyes and faces.
- The membrane covering the opening to some lizards' earholes is called the tympanum (the name also given to the skin covering a drum). It vibrates to sound.
- Most Australian lizards eat insects and other small animals. Monitors will eat carrion. Larger skinks and dragons may eat some vegetable material.
- Australian lizards are harmless to humans. Some will gape and hiss when cornered, but they prefer escape to confrontation.
- The world's largest lizard is the Komodo Dragon (a monitor lizard) of several small Indonesian islands. A specimen 3.10 m long weighed 166 kg.

A Yellow-spotted Monitor tastes the air with its long, forked tongue

DID YOU KNOW?

FACTS ABOUT HOT AND COLD LIZARDS

- When cold, a lizard will bask in the sunlight, warming its body. Some lizards turn dark to help them absorb heat.
- Some lizards have permanent black markings on their heads and black stripes down their backs. These markings speed heat to the lizard's brain and spine.
- When a lizard is warm enough, it moves to shade or other shelter.
- Dragons sit on basking-perches to watch over their territories. They may sleep on their perches and thus use the first rays of the sun to warm up their bodies.
- Desert lizards may spend the heat of the day in a burrow, or under a rock. They hunt in the early morning or in the late afternoon.

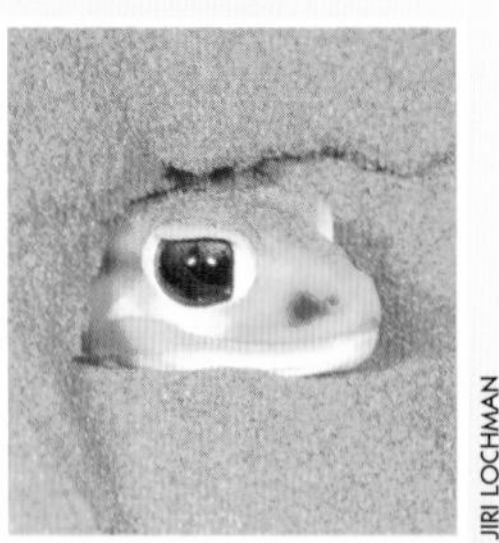

JIRI LOCHMAN

Smooth Knob-tailed Gecko emerging from its burrow

How lizards live and behave

In order to exploit a wide variety of ecological niches*, Australia's lizards have adopted many different lifestyles. Like other reptiles, lizards spend much of their time in regulating the temperatures of their bodies. They form prey for many other animals and most smaller species are constantly on the lookout for would-be predators. These behaviours, and the ways in which lizards obtain food and reproduce themselves, are looked at more closely in the discussion of the five groups on pages 44–57.

An Australian food chain

Especially in its warmer areas, Australia is home to enormous numbers of termites. They "graze" on all sorts of plant materials, just as antelopes and deer do in other countries. In the termites' guts live tiny organisms which can break down the tough plant materials most animals cannot digest.

Small lizards, snakes and frogs feed on these abundant termites. They in turn form prey for larger reptiles, plus carnivorous mammals and all sorts of birds.

IAN MORRIS

Central Bearded Dragon basking on a perch

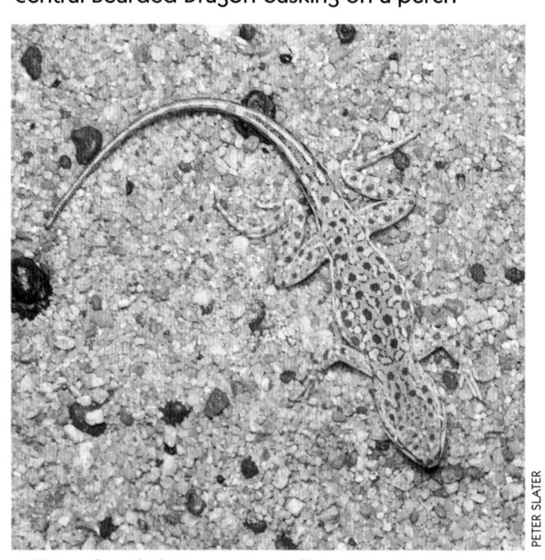

PETER SLATER

Military Sand-dragon camouflaged on pebbles

JIRI LOCHMAN

Eastern Water Dragon lives near creeks and swamps

Southern Forest Dragon camouflaged on lichen

HOW TO TELL A LIZARD FROM A SNAKE

ALL SNAKES	MOST LIZARDS	A FEW LIZARDS
lack limbs (pythons have traces)	have limbs	have reduced or no limbs, or hindlimb flaps
lack ear-openings	have ear-openings or tympanic membranes	have scaly depressions instead of ear-openings
have long, slender, forked tongues	have fleshy tongues which may be notched	have long, slender forked tongues (monitors)
lack eyelids	have movable lower eyelids	have immovable lower eyelids (legless lizards, geckos and some skinks)
have length from snout to vent much greater than from vent to tailtip	have length from snout to vent less than vent to tailtip	can lose their tails and regenerate much shorter ones (geckos, some skinks, some legless lizards)
have single or enlarged belly scales (except file snakes and blind snakes)	have small underbody scales which are nearly equal in size to body scales	have large underbody scales arranged in pairs (some legless lizards)

JIRI LOCHMAN

Australia's largest monitor, the Perentie, like most lizards, swallows its food whole. Here one eats a bettong, a small ground-living relative of the kangaroo

FACTS

- Lizards do not chew their food, but swallow it whole. Some, like legless lizards, break off pieces by thrashing the prey from side to side or "death-rolling" with it.
- Some geckos and legless lizards squeak, squawk or yap when they are startled or interacting socially. Monitors may hiss when threatened.
- The Perentie, the largest Australian lizard, grows to 2.5 m and may weigh 15 kg.
- The scientific name of the Perentie, *Varanus giganteus*, means "giant monitor".
- Most lizards lay eggs, which are incubated in the soil or under litter.
- The females of some species of skinks retain their eggs in their bodies until hatching.

IAN MORRIS

A Red-sided Rainbow-skink hatching

DID YOU KNOW?

FACTS

- Geckos' closest relatives are the legless lizards. The two groups look quite different, but many of their internal body features are the same and they often behave in similar ways.

UNDERSIDES OF GECKO FEET

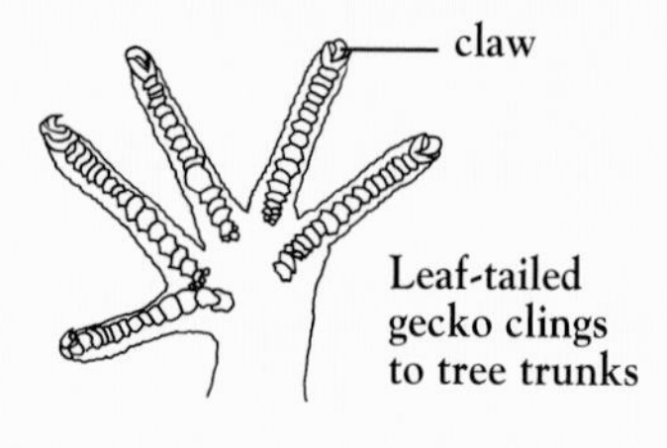

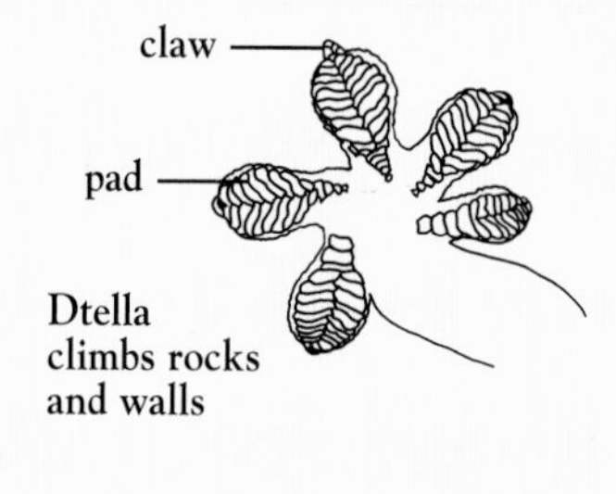

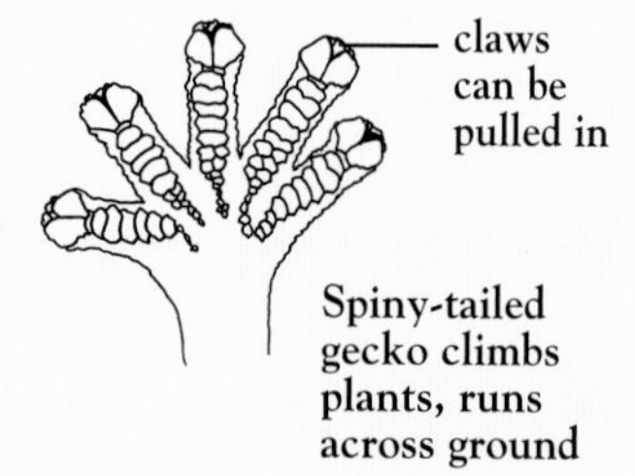

Soft skins, wide eyes

Rough Knob-tailed Gecko

There are close to 100 species of Australian geckos. Their soft skins range in texture from velvety to rough. Their large eyes are protected by fixed, transparent lower eyelids.

All geckos have five fingers and five toes. In climbing species, these digits end in pads which cling to smooth, slick surfaces, and in ground-living species they end in claws, which may retract cat-fashion. Some geckos have both pads and claws.

Geckos are active after dusk. The pupil of the eye is a vertical slit, which opens wide in low light and may close to a series of pinholes in daylight. Geckos have easily-seen earholes. They are quite vocal and may squeak or squawk loudly when seized. When defending their territories against other geckos of the same species, they chatter loudly. Female geckos produce just a few large eggs in a clutch, but may lay several clutches in a breeding season.

These lizards are efficient predators, which will seize and swallow any animal small enough to subdue, including other geckos. They take only moving prey.

Knobs on their tails

There are seven species of knob-tail geckos. They are large (sometimes as long as an adult human hand), with short, knob-ended tails which are twitched when their owners are alarmed. Knob-tail geckos have enormous heads and powerful jaws, which deal easily with their prey of insects, spiders, scorpions and other geckos.

The Rough Knob-tailed Gecko of northern Australia has warty skin, which camouflages it on pebbly soil. It stalks its prey with a jerky, swaying walk, that resembles leaves blowing in the breeze, before making a final rush. This gecko's scientific name, *Nephrurus asper*, means "rough kidney-tail", referring to the texture of its skin and its plump, curved end-piece.

When threatened, the Rough Knob-tail inflates with air, making itself look larger, then does push-ups, edging away sideways from the threat while carrying out its bluff.

The Jewelled Gecko climbs around in *Triodia* spinifex clumps

The Three-lined Knob-tailed Gecko stalks insects and other geckos

This Chameleon Gecko has its original, white-banded tail. Regenerated tails are speckled brown

The Northern Spiny-tailed Gecko is a tail-squirter which occurs in northwestern Australia

The Southwestern Spiny-tailed Gecko is a tail-squirter with colourful eyes

Tales of tails

Gecko tails vary greatly in shape and in size in comparison to the owners' bodies. A mature male gecko can be identified by two large bulges on the underside of the base of the tail.

Like a cat, a gecko will twitch its tail when frightened or aggressive. Most geckos will drop some or all of the tail when attacked, when fighting or even when mating. The replacement tail may be a different colour, or lack the markings of the original. Some species have prehensile* tails; some store fat in their tails in times of plenty, then use it for nourishment in lean seasons.

To defend themselves, some geckos squirt fluid from glands in their tails, sometimes to a distance of 30 centimetres. The fluid is distasteful, irritating and forms sticky threads, deterring a predator from further attack. A tail-squirting gecko may be able to "fire" several times in succession.

Gecko goggles

A gecko's transparent lower eyelids cover its eyeballs and are fused to the upper eyelids, giving it an unblinking stare.

These protective "goggles" prevent the surface of the large eyes drying out. The eyes cannot be cleaned by tears and eyelid movement, and must be frequently washed by the gecko's long tongue.

This Marbled Velvet Gecko cannot blink

FACTS

- The Chameleon Gecko of Queensland rainforests from Tully to Cooktown stalks its prey with slow, deliberate movements. It may take one hour to get within grabbing distance of its victim.
- The Northern Spiny-tailed Gecko is a tail-squirter which occurs through the northwestern two-thirds of Australia. It lives in trees and spinifex and grows to around 15 cm in length. The female lays two soft-shelled eggs per clutch.
- A gecko's broad, flat tongue is used to groom its eyes and head. Some species of geckos also use their tongues to lick nectar from flowers. These species carry pollen between the flowers on which they feed.

DID YOU KNOW?

FACTS

- At night, when dtellas hunt, they are pale in colour. During the day, they darken to match as closely as possible the colour and shade of their background.
- Some geckos make loud territorial calls. In South-East Asia, gamblers lay bets on the number of calls a gecko will make in a given time.

No males required!

Females of a few species of geckos reproduce without mating with males (this is known as parthenogenetic* reproduction). There are no males in these species, as only female sex cells are available. Some blind snakes reproduce in the same fashion.

Geckos are vocal and active when courting. Females lay one or two eggs at a time, in a succession of clutches. Several females may deposit eggs in a communal nest. The eggs may have parchment-like or brittle shells. The eggs of some species are slightly adhesive, so that they stick together.

IAN MORRIS

This Leaf-tailed Gecko mimics the colour of the tree trunk

IAN MORRIS

The Cave Prickly Gecko is an agile climber which can tackle a nearly vertical wall

IAN MORRIS

The Variegated Dtella is pale when it hunts at night and darkens during the day

Geckos that live in houses

The dtellas are climbing geckos which have claws arching over the pads at the tips of their digits. They are found on tree trunks, rock faces and walls of buildings. The house-dwellers catch insects attracted to electric lights.

The Top-end Dtella inhabits the walls of houses across the Top End and the Kimberley, while a gecko catching insects under a porch light in coastal Queensland is likely to be the Dubious Dtella. The House Gecko occurs in the world's tropical regions. It lives in or around houses, taking insects attracted to lights at night. In Australia, the House Gecko is spreading southwards from its first colonies in Darwin and Cape York and can now be found in Brisbane. This species disappears from houses abandoned by humans.

The Cape York Pad-tail Gecko has special scales under its tail which help the owner grip surfaces it is climbing

IAN MORRIS

The Giant Cave Gecko of northern Australia lives on sandstone. This one is crawling across Aboriginal rock art

Limbless wonders

Thirty-three of the world's 35 species of legless lizard are found only in Australia. One species is found in New Guinea as well as Australia, and one occurs only in New Guinea.

Burton's Legless Lizard eats other lizards

JIRI LOCHMAN

Legless lizards are related to geckos. Their eyelids are transparent and fused, like those of geckos, and are cleaned with the tongue.

Most species of legless lizards have an external ear opening, but some burrowing ones have concealed ears. They have no front limbs and the hindlimbs are reduced to flaps on either side of the vent. The shiny body scales overlap and the tail is long in proportion to the body. A legless lizard may shed enough of its tail to distract a predator. The tail later regenerates; the regrown part is rarely as long as the original and may be brighter in colour.

The least commonly seen legless lizards are the worm-lizards, which are burrowers with shiny scales, cylindrical bodies and rounded tailtips.

Legless lizards may resemble snakes, but are harmless to humans. They move more slowly and smoothly than snakes. All species are protectively coloured and most burrow in loose ground litter or just under the soil surface.

Death-rollers

Some legless lizards feed on insects, spiders and their egg cases. If the prey is too large to swallow, the lizard grabs it in its jaws, then "death rolls" with it like a small crocodile, tearing off pieces small enough to eat. The lizard may also lap up the body fluids of the prey. Some legless lizard species lick up nectar from flowers. These species will also eat berries and fruits.

DID YOU KNOW?

FACTS

- The tail of a legless lizard may be up to 2.5 times as long as its body.
- The small, rare Adorned Delma of southeast Queensland is 15 cm in length.
- The large Southern Scaly-foot can grow to 85 cm in length.
- Burton's Legless Lizard may grow to 62 cm. It is found over most of Australia and its colour and pattern vary widely from place to place.
- Burton's Legless Lizard preys on other lizards. It has a long snout and sharp, hinged teeth, which stab into even the hard, shiny scales of skinks. Its skull is flexible, allowing it to seize and swallow large prey.

IAN MORRIS

The Rusty-topped Delma is a "flick-leaping" legless lizard which lives in northern Australia. Its tail accounts for three-quarters of its total length

Southern Scaly-foot bluffing by rearing up, puffing its throat, hissing and flicking its tongue

When threatened by larger animals, legless lizards have few defences and rely on bluff to scare off predators. Some bark or squeak when touched. Some "flick-leap" in sudden, jerky bounds. Some behave in ways that take advantage of their snake-like appearance. Their markings mimic those of the more dangerous reptiles and if threatened they behave like snakes, hissing with their heads raised, throats puffed and tongues flicking in and out. If hard-pressed, they may even strike like snakes, though they have no fangs and no venom apparatus.*

The Unbanded Shovel-nosed Snake shows the dark head and nape markings possessed by many small snakes

The Western Scaly-foot is a legless lizard which mimics a snake

FACTS

- Worm-lizards have shiny scales. They live in earth cracks, under logs and in ant nests. When attacked, a worm-lizard holds its tailtip up and moves it about, then sheds it to distract the predator.
- Members of the delma group escape danger by "flick-leaping". They fling their bodies into up-and-down waves and move forward by flicking their tails.
- Most legless lizards lay two eggs in a clutch. Females of some species may lay their eggs together in a nest.
- The Bronzeback, a burrowing legless lizard from the arid inland, was first noted by scientists in the 1890s and not seen again until 1978.

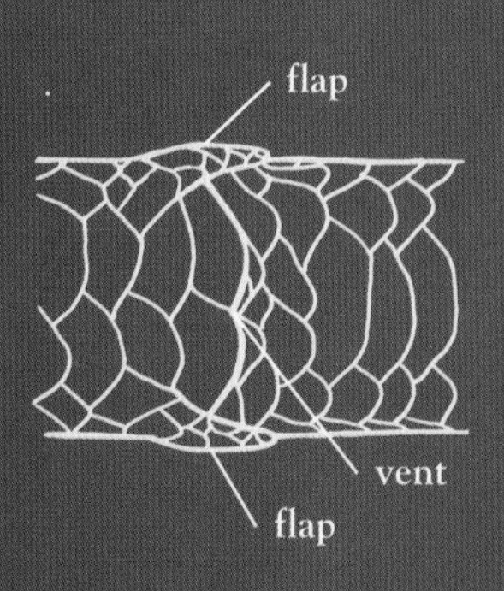

Underside of a legless lizard, showing the flap feet on the sides just in front of the vent

DID YOU KNOW?

FACTS

- The largest Australian dragon lizard is the Frilled Lizard. Head and body of a big "Frilly" can measure nearly 30 cm, the tail adds almost 70 cm and the frill can measure up to 30 cm across.
- The huge Komodo "Dragon" of Indonesia is not a dragon at all, but a monitor (goanna).
- Most dragons are active by day, though a few desert species may hunt after dusk.
- Dragons eat any moving creature small enough to be swallowed. Larger dragons may also eat some plant material. The Thorny Devil of Australia's deserts eats only small black ants.

Here be dragons

The Southern Forest Dragon of southern Qld and northern NSW rainforests

Australia has about 65 of the world's approximately 330 species of dragon lizards. They are commonest in the warmer and more arid regions of the continent.

Dragons have four well developed limbs, each with five clawed digits. The hindlimbs are usually longer than the forelimbs and some species stand upright and can run on them. The scales on a dragon's body and legs are small and rough. On the upper surface of the reptile the scales may be spiny or keeled and in some species the scales over the spine are enlarged to form a crest. There are folds of skin above and below the eyes which, with movable eyelids and special brow scales, protect the eyes from harsh sunlight. The pupils are round and most dragons hunt by day.

The ear opening of most species is covered by a tympanum. The tongue is short and fleshy. It is broad, flat and often slightly sticky.

A dragon's tail is usually slender, tapering, and longer than the owner's snout-to-vent length. A dragon cannot shed its tail voluntarily. If part of the tail is broken off by a predator or by accident, only a limited amount will regrow.

All dragons lay parchment-shelled eggs. Male dragons, and the females of a few species, have pores under their thighs and in front of their vents. A waxy substance from these pores leaves signals which other dragons can receive with their tongues.

PETER SLATER

Open-mouthed, the Central Bearded Dragon bluffs a predator, flattening its body and expanding its throat into a "beard"

RAOUL SLATER

Dragons such as this Gilbert's Lashtail have perches they use regularly as display points or sunning spots

IAN MORRIS

The Canegrass Two-lined Dragon of central Australia climbs into a bush to escape ground-level heat

A Ring-tailed Bicycle-dragon basking in the early morning sunshine

Sitting in the sunshine, sheltering in the shade

In cool conditions, or early in the morning, a dragon may lie in the open or on a perch, flatten its body and bask. Its skin darkens, taking in heat more readily. As the dragon's temperature rises, its colour lightens. It may angle its body to reduce the surface exposed to the sun.

When warm, the lizard seeks shelter in a burrow or rock crevice, or climbs into vegetation, where the air temperature is much lower than on the ground. In the open, some desert dragons raise their bodies until only the heels of their hindfeet and claws of their forefeet touch the heated ground. A few hold one limb in the air, or rise on their hindlegs. The frill of the Frilled Lizard is thought to help disperse heat from the body, as well as bluffing predators and being used in displays.

Dragons on display

Many species of dragons have crests, or folds of loose skin on their bodies. When threatened, they may stand their ground, flattening or puffing out their bodies, opening their mouths and erecting "beards" or neck-frills.

Dragons communicate with each other by body language. A male dragon may establish a territory, with a perch on which it arm-waves, head-bobs and postures at other dragons. Dominant male dragons may display bright colour-patches.

The Frilled Lizard extends its frill in bluff

FACTS

- The Ring-tailed Bicycle-dragon occurs in rocky places across northern Australia. When chasing low-flying insects, it may run on its hindlegs and leap to catch its prey in mid-air.
- Desert dragons may drink water which falls as rain or collects as dew on their tails and bodies. The drops are channelled to their mouths along grooves between their scales.
- If unmolested, species such as the Eastern Water Dragon and various bearded dragons will live in house gardens and public parks.
- One fat Eastern Water Dragon lived for 12 years in a Brisbane car-sale premises situated in the middle of a busy traffic roundabout. "George" eventually disappeared, probably "dragon-napped" by an admirer.

DID YOU KNOW?

FACTS

- The Swamplands Lashtail of the Top End of the NT hides under ground-litter during the Dry and emerges to breed just before the Wet season. Between four and six eggs are laid above the floodline.
- The Superb Two-lined Dragon of the Kimberley Division has a tail which may be over four times as long as head and body combined.
- The Central Netted Dragon lives in arid northwestern and central Australia. Periods of heat or cold are spent in a back-filled burrow. Of 1000 individuals marked in a WA study, only about 2% survived past one year.

STANLEY BREEDEN

The Swamplands Lashtail of Northern Territory wetlands

IAN MORRIS

Boyd's Forest Dragon is camouflaged in the rainforest

Dragons in the rainforest

Rainforest dragons are camouflaged by their coloration, their crests and their angle-headed outlines.

These dragons will circle a tree trunk to stay on the other side as an intruder walks past. Boyd's Forest Dragon grows to 50 centimetres long and occurs in northeastern Queensland. The Southern Forest Dragon lives in coastal southern Queensland and northern New South Wales. In the breeding season, Southern Forest Dragon males engage in ritual combat, puffing out bodies and throats, standing high on their legs and circling each other. From December to January, a group of females may lay their eggs together in an earth bank.

Spiky anteater

The Thorny Devil of the arid inland, which feeds on small black ants, can slowly change its colour to match its background. When attacked, this harmless lizard bends its head down, so the knob on its neck forms a false head.

JIRI LOCHMAN

A Central Netted Ground-dragon stands tall to avoid the heat of the ground

The Eastern Water Dragon lives in creeks and waterways

The colours of lizards

A Thorny Devil on a background of beige sand

The Thorny Devil changes colour to match red sand

JIRI LOCHMAN

The Superb Two-lined Dragon's lime-green colour acts as camouflage amongst leaves, as well as signalling its status to other dragons

IAN MORRIS

The Western Netted Ground-dragon changes colour and pattern as it ages. Other dragons respond to these visual signals

A lizard's skin contains black pigment cells, which expand to make the skin darker, or contract to make it lighter. Many dragons and geckos can change colour quite quickly, according to their mood or activity, or in response to the intensity of light. These changes are useful in temperature regulation, for camouflage and for signalling to other lizards. Lizards of one species may vary in colour and pattern from place to place, and a lizard regularly sheds old skin to reveal new, brighter skin.

MONITORS

The watchful ones

Australia is home to 25 of the world's approximately 30 species of monitors (also known as goannas). They are active daytime hunters and formidable predators, whose tails, teeth and claws are used as offensive and defensive weapons.

A monitor is covered with small, non-overlapping scales. The limbs are powerful and each has five clawed digits. Many species are good climbers.

Monitors have keen senses. They have external earholes and movable eyelids. The long, forked tongue retrieves scent particles to an area on the roof of the mouth which sends signals to the brain.

Gould's Monitor is common on mainland Australia

If mutilated, a monitor's tail does not grow again.

During the breeding season, male monitors may engage in territorial fights, head-feinting, tail-lashing and wrestling with each other.

These two male Perenties are wrestling in territorial dispute

DID YOU KNOW?

FACTS

- "Monitors" were so-named because they were thought to watch and warn of the presence of crocodiles. The name "goanna" also used for monitors comes from the word "iguana" which was originally the Spanish *l'iguane*, meaning lizard.
- The Perentie, the largest Australian monitor, may grow to 2.5 m in length and weigh up to 15 kg. It is found from the central WA coast across inland Australia.
- Gould's Monitor is found throughout mainland Australia, except for the extreme southern coast. It prefers sandy soils, where it digs burrows.
- The Lace Monitor of eastern Australia may grow to 2 m in length. It is a tree-climber, which may visit campsites in search of scraps.

Lace Monitor

STANLEY BREEDEN

The Yellow-spotted Monitor, like all the monitor group, eats carrion when it is available

JIRI LOCHMAN

A Spotted Tree Monitor eats frogs and birds

Merten's Water Monitor of northern Australia

Monitor nurseries

A male monitor is a persistent suitor, following a female around until she accepts him. They then mate a number of times. The female monitor will lay between two and 12 eggs.

Some species of monitors lay in ground or arboreal* termite mounds. After the eggs are laid, the egg chamber is sealed by the termites. The hatchlings would be too feeble to dig their way out of the extremely hard material of which the nest is constructed, so they remain in their eggs until the mound is opened again the following breeding season by a female about to lay her eggs inside. Then the young hatch within a day and leave the mound before the termites reseal the chamber.

Some monitors lay in a hole dug into soil, under a stone or log. A female Gould's Monitor plugs the entrance to her nesting burrow with soil. The young will take up to 265 days to emerge.

A Black-palmed Rock Monitor hunting

IAN MORRIS

FACTS

- The largest living lizard, the Komodo Dragon, can grow to more than 3 m in length. Its tail is half its total length. Salvadori's Monitor (found in New Guinea) may be longer, but its tail makes up two-thirds of its length.
- Fossil monitor lizards dating to the Upper Cretaceous (95–65 million years ago), have been found in North America. However, no monitors live there now.
- All monitors can swim. Merten's and Mitchell's Water Monitors, the Rusty Monitor and the Mangrove Monitor live and find their food near salt or fresh water.
- Spotted Tree Monitors are camouflaged in colours and patterns which match the tree trunks on which they live. This northern Australian monitor eats lizards, frogs, cicadas and fledgling birds.

DID YOU KNOW?

FACTS

- The spiny-tailed skinks are active during the day. When threatened, spiny-tailed skinks wedge themselves into refuges by inflating their bodies so their spines hold them in place.
- Smallest spiny-tailed skink is the Pygmy Spiny-tailed Skink (16 cm in length). The large King's Skink (over 60 cm) lives on the coastal islands of southwestern Western Australia. It may eat seabird eggs and chicks.
- Many spiny-tailed skinks deposit their droppings on one "toilet" site near their burrow. One theory is that this attracts insects, which the lizard then eats.
- Rainbow-skinks have scales which have an iridescent sheen. During the breeding season, males become brightly coloured on heads and sides.
- Mulch-skinks and bar-lipped skinks live under leaf-litter and have long bodies, short limbs and long, strong tails.

Lizard all-sorts

IAN MORRIS

Pygmy Spiny-tailed Skink

Approximately 300 of the world's 1300 species of skinks live in Australia and many of our best-known reptiles, from tiny striped "garden lizards" to large blue-tongues, are skinks. The skink family includes lizards of many shapes and sizes, which are adapted to a variety of habitats and lifestyles.

Skinks usually have smooth, flat, overlapping scales, though some have ridged scales. Some skinks have movable eyelids, others have the transparent lower lid fused to the upper lid. The ear opening is usually present, but in some sand-swimming skinks it may be very small, or hidden. The tongue is broad and fleshy.

Skinks which run and climb have well developed limbs, but many burrowing species have reduced digits and limbs.

Most skinks readily drop their tails in self-defence, though a few larger species cannot do so. Most lay eggs, but some living in cooler climates are live-bearers*.

JIRI LOCHMAN

The Gidgee Spiny-tailed Skink of the Abrolhos Is.

IAN MORRIS

The Closed-litter Rainbow-skink lives on the forest floor

Soil-swimmers and leaf-litter lurkers

Sandsliders are skinks with less than the normal numbers of limbs, fingers and toes. They have slippery scales and "swim" under the surface by burrowing with the snout and wriggling from side to side. Worm-skinks have round bodies, reduced or no limbs, and shiny scales. Some have the scales on the snout fused to form a soil-pushing shield.

IAN MORRIS

The Southern Sandslider "swims" through sand

A Centralian Bluetongue gapes to show its bright tongue when threatened

There are five species of bluetongue skinks found in Australia. They have smooth scales, flattened striped bodies and pointed tails. They eat insects and soft plants and show their bright tongues in warning. Female bluetongues bear between two and seven live young in summer.

The Shingleback Lizard, which is found across southern Australia, has "pine-cone" scales, a stumpy, fat-storing tail and a blue tongue. It feeds on vegetation and insects and the female gives birth to two, or sometimes three, large live young in summer.

The Shingleback Lizard is a large, rough-scaled skink which gives birth to live young

The Prickly Forest Skink has keeled scales

Comb-ears

Australia has at least 70 species of *Ctenotus* skinks, fast-running lizards patterned in stripes and spots. The word *ctenotus* means "comb-ear" and refers to the bumps on the front edge of the ear-opening.

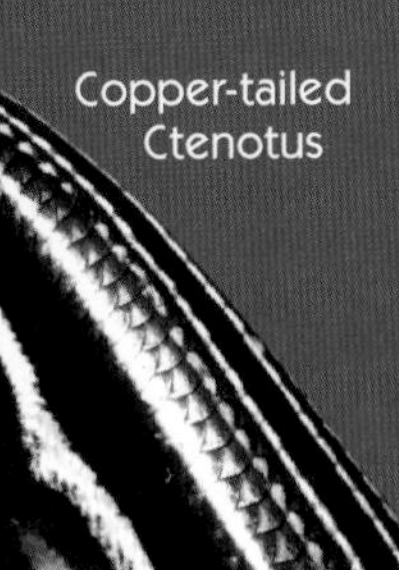

Copper-tailed Ctenotus

FACTS

- The Adelaide Pygmy Bluetongue had not been seen since 1959 and was thought to be extinct when Graham Armstrong opened up a snake squashed by a car near Burra, SA, in 1992. In the snake, he found the body of an Adelaide Pygmy Bluetongue. A search of the area revealed a colony of the elusive skinks.
- The Prickly Forest Skink lives in wet areas in northeastern Qld. It forages for snails, slugs, insect larvae and worms. Each of its small scales is keeled and has a backwards facing point.
- The Copper-tailed Ctenotus was one of the first Australian lizards to be recorded by scientists, in 1790. Its scientific name, *Ctenotus taeniolatus*, means "ribbon-sided comb-ear".

What is a snake?

A snake is a long, slender, limbless reptile. (One group of snakes, the pythons, has claw-like remnants of hindlimbs.) The body and tail are supported by a backbone, which may contain more than 400 vertebrae.

A snake's tail is always shorter than its head and body combined. If damaged, it does not regrow.

Most snakes' scales are smooth and overlapping. The belly scales are larger than the other body scales, except in blind and file snakes.

A snake's eyes have limited movement in their sockets and are covered by fixed transparent scales, which are shed at intervals when the skin is sloughed. There is no external ear and the inner ear is not efficient, though snakes are very sensitive to vibrations. They also learn about their surroundings through vision (though many burrowing snakes have limited sight), smell and taste (chemical traces are carried by the forked tongue to a receptor in the roof of the mouth). All but two of Australia's python species have pits which are sensitive to infra-red (heat) radiation on their faces.

In some groups of snakes, venom glands in the head supply grooved or hollow fangs, which introduce the venom into anything bitten. Snakes which lack venom generally crush their prey in their jaws or constrict it in their coils.

Most snakes lay eggs (pythons may "incubate" them) but some give birth to live young.

The non-venomous Green Tree Snake is an acrobatic climber

Snake eyes

Most vertebrates, including humans and lizards, focus their eyes by moving muscles which push the lens out of its normal shape. Snakes focus their eyes differently, by moving the lens around to varying positions in front of the retina*.

There is a theory that ancestral snakes burrowed and had minute or non-functioning eyes. The groups of snakes which emerged to hunt in the light re-invented the eye. Most day-hunting snakes have fair-sized eyes, while nocturnal hunters rely more on scent and body heat to track prey and tend to have smaller eyes.

SPOT THE DIFFERENCES

The Eastern Tiger is a venomous front-fanged snake

JIRI LOCHMAN

The Olive Python is a non-venomous constricting snake

A Stimson's Python swallowing a rodent it has constricted and suffocated

The rear-fanged Northern Brown Tree Snake has weak venom but powerful jaws

Australia's seven snake families

Worldwide, there are 12 families of snakes. Seven are found in Australia.

BLIND SNAKES are small, cylindrical, smooth-scaled, burrowing snakes, which eat soft insects. Australia has around 30 species.

PYTHONS are non-venomous snakes which kill prey by coiling around it and suffocating it. Australia has 15 species.

COLUBRID* (REAR-FANGED) SNAKES may have fangs at the backs of their mouths. Some are non-venomous, some venomous. Australia has 11 species.

ELAPID* OR FRONT-FANGED SNAKES inject venom efficiently through fangs at the front of the mouth. Australia has around 75 species, about 20 of which are potentially harmful to humans, though today fatalities are rare.

FILE SNAKES have rasp-like skin covered with keeled scales and are non-venomous fish-eaters. There are two northern species in Australia.

SEASNAKES live in coastal waters. They are paddle-tailed snakes which have venom glands and fangs like those of front-fanged snakes. Most are potentially harmful to humans. Over 30 species frequent Australian waters.

SEA KRAITS are banded, venomous, marine snakes which emerge on land to bask or rest, but feed at sea. Two species may occur near Australia.

FACTS

- The oldest fossil snake found so far, from Algeria, has been dated to about 120 million years ago.
- A constricting snake which was up to 6 m long lived in western Queensland more than 40 million years ago. It may have survived until two million years ago.
- A snake's internal organs are shaped to fit its elongate body. One lung is often larger than the other and does most or all the breathing.
- A snake moves by throwing its body into loops, then pushing itself forward by pressing the back part of each loop against the ground. Moving across sand, a snake may "side-wind", by throwing loops of its body sideways.

The small front-fanged snakes, such as this Southern Desert Banded Snake, are harmless to humans

The front-fanged Northern Death Adder's long fangs hold its prey while injecting venom

How snakes live and behave

A snake will move between several places in its living area as a year proceeds. One reason for a shift in location may be keeping the body temperature stable (preferably around 30°C), for a snake's long, slender body heats or cools rapidly. Other reasons for a shift in locale could be finding food, finding a mate and avoiding danger.

Snakes alternate short periods of activity with lengthy periods of lying quietly coiled in some sheltered place. When inactive, they can go without food for considerable periods.

Smaller species of snakes eat invertebrates and tiny lizards. Larger species eat vertebrates, including other snakes. Prey is detected by sight (except for groups with less efficient eyes), by sensing vibration and by following minute chemical traces picked up by the hunter's forked tongue then transferred to the receptor in the palate. Most Australian pythons have facial pits which detect heat and help them track mammals or birds. The victim is immobilised by constriction, or by injection of venom, or both.

Snakes are generally solitary, but individuals of some species may be found sheltering together in very cold weather. In the mating season, the males of some species engage in combat. A male snake has two half-penises, called hemipenes*, which lie inside sheaths at the base of its tail and emerge when needed. When mating, the male uses the hemipenis on the side nearest the female. Many snake species lay leathery-shelled eggs (some in communal nests). Around one-quarter of Australian species give birth to live young.

JIRI LOCHMAN

Children's Python was named after J.G. Children, an English naturalist. It plucks flying bats from the air as they enter or leave their roosting caves

The halves of a snake's lower jaw separate to let the head engulf prey. As the snake's body expands, skin can be seen between the scales

The decoy

A hungry snake may seek prey by actively searching, or by waiting in ambush for prey of a suitable size. The death adders are ambushers which add their own special touch. A death adder coils in hiding, wiggling the light-coloured end of its tail near its head. A small animal checking out the tempting tail tip is seized and injected with venom.

The "lure" is the tail tip of a Northern Death Adder held just in front of its mouth

Open wide!

A snake can swallow prey which is wider than its jaws.

The bones in a snake's head, except for those protecting the brain, can move back and forth on each other and the snake can "disconnect" the halves of its lower jaw, so they remain joined only by elastic ligaments*. The snake grips its prey with one side of its lower jaw, then moves the other side forward. It hitches its upper jaw forward, then repeats the process. It can breathe because its windpipe ends in a snorkel-like extension. As the prey passes down the body, the snake's ribs separate widely.

THREE TYPES OF SNAKE DENTITION*

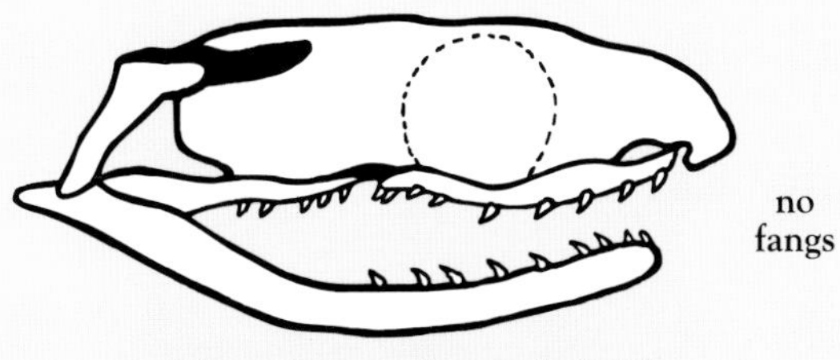

Most Australian colubrids

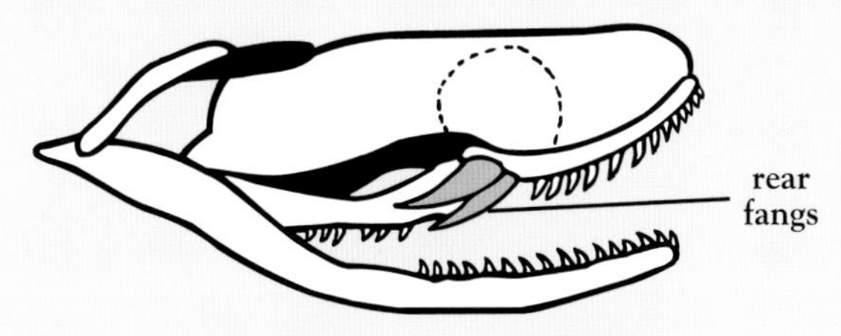

Some Australian colubrids

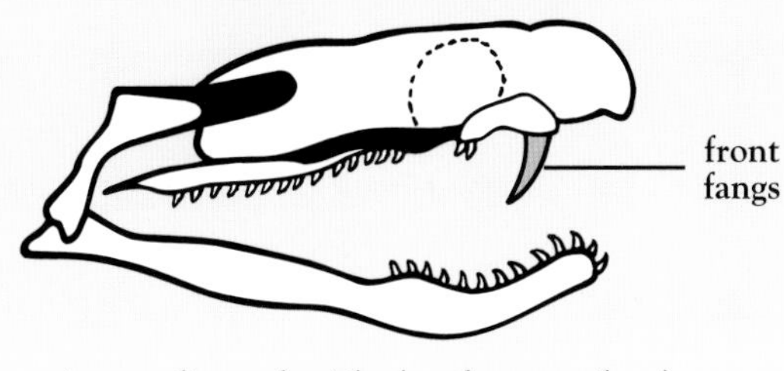

Australian elapids (and seasnakes)

Many Australian snakes belong to the colubrid* family. Most Australian colubrids have no venom glands. Their teeth are solid and they have no fangs. A few colubrids have venom glands which eject venom through fangs at the *backs* of their jaws. Though venomous, they are not seen as dangerous to humans.

Many other Australian snakes belong to the elapid* family. They have venom glands leading to fixed fangs at the *fronts* of their jaws. Some of the Australian elapids are extremely dangerous, and potentially lethal to humans. However, most species are only mildly venomous and are not regarded as dangerous to humans.

Seasnakes deliver venom in the same way as elapids do.

FACTS

- Different species of animal react differently to snake venom. A lizard may survive 100 times the amount of venom which would kill a mouse of similar weight.
- Many of Australia's dangerous snakes have comparatively short fangs but very toxic* venom.
- The fork at the end of a snake's tongue may act as a direction-finder when the owner tracks down prey. The snake may follow the path indicated by the fork-end which "tastes" the stronger scent-trace.

IAN MORRIS

A Western Brown Snake, an elapid, ready to strike

- Longest Australian elapid snake is the Taipan, at around 3 m, but the heaviest is probably the sturdy-bodied Mulga (King Brown) Snake.
- Some venomous snakes which have short fangs throw coils around their prey to hold it while they inject sufficient venom to kill it.

DID YOU KNOW?

FACTS ABOUT FILE SNAKES

- A female file snake is much fuller-bodied and heavier than a male of the same length. She hunts in deeper water and takes larger prey than the male does.
- Arafura File Snakes concentrate in permanent water in the floodplains of the Top End, Gulf of Carpentaria and eastern Cape York during the Dry season.

Skins like rasps

The seasonally flooded coastal wetlands of northern Australia are home to two of the world's three species of file snakes. These non-venomous snakes have skin covered by sharp-pointed or finely keeled scales which do not overlap. The loose skin has a rasp-like texture.

File snakes have deep, narrow bodies and semi-prehensile tails. They take about one-fifth of their oxygen requirements from the water through their skins and poke their heads above water to take in air through valved nostrils. An Arafura File Snake will anchor its tail to an underwater projection and seize a passing fish with its recurved teeth, absorbing the impact with its elastic body. Its rough skin grips the fish firmly and the victim soon succumbs to constriction. The Little File Snake eats less active fish, such as gobies and mudskippers.

IAN MORRIS

The Little File Snake lives in mangroves and swamps, feeding on fish, crabs and snails

IAN MORRIS

On a Top End floodplain, an Aboriginal hunter displays two Arafura File Snakes

Bush tucker

The Aboriginal people of Australia's Top End hunt file snakes at the end of the Dry season by wading into drying billabongs and feeling under logs, weeds and banks for the rough-skinned reptiles. The snake is thrown onto the bank, or killed by biting the back of the neck then stretching the body downward.

STANLEY BREEDEN

File snakes have sharp-pointed or finely keeled scales, giving the skin a rasp-like texture. Note the small tongue of this Arafura File Snake

IAN MORRIS

The Blackish Blind Snake is Australia's largest blind snake

BLIND SNAKES

The burrowers

Australia has over 30 species of round-bodied, smooth-scaled blind snakes. They are rarely seen except when earth, stones or logs are turned over, or when they appear on the surface after rain.

These snakes have poorly developed eyes and can probably only detect the difference between darkness and light. The glossy scales overlap considerably, which protects against soil abrasion and increases the rigidity of the body. Glands in head and neck secrete oily substances which lubricate the body as it burrows. The mouth lies well under the blunt snout and the tongue is small and forked. The short tail (less than 5 per cent of the total length) ends in a spine, used to anchor the snake as it shovels with its snout.

FACTS

- Two to six male Arafura File Snakes will form a mating cluster with a single female. About 11 months after mating, she gives birth to 6–27 young.
- An Arafura File Snake may not reproduce until 9 years old, then may go up to 10 years between clutches of young. One captive female gave birth to a young one after 7 years on her own.

ABOUT BLIND SNAKES

- The muscles of a blind snake's forebody are enlarged and the snake "pulls" itself through the soil like an engine pulling a train.
- Blind snakes do not have enlarged belly scales like most other snakes.
- Some blind snakes are found in ant or termite nests. A blind snake can follow an ant trail by scent a week after the ants have gone.
- The introduced Flowerpot Blind Snake is parthenogenetic, females producing only females. At 12 cm, it is the smallest snake found in Australia.

Squeeze, then eat

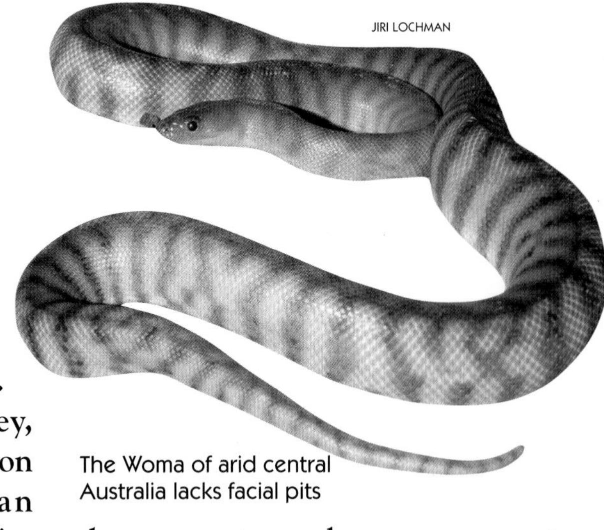

JIRI LOCHMAN

The Woma of arid central Australia lacks facial pits

Australia's 15 species of pythons have long, pointed, razor-sharp teeth and lack venom glands. They throw coils around their prey, then kill it by constriction. A python suffocates its prey, rather than crushing it. Every time the victim breathes out, the python tightens its coils.

Pythons' eyes have vertical pupils and they are generally night hunters. Thirteen species of Australian pythons have facial pits which detect changes in heat and allow the python to track warm-blooded mammals and birds. The other two, which have no pits, hunt mainly reptiles.

Climbing species of python have prehensile tails. Both sexes have short spurs near the vent. The remnants of hind limbs, they are used by the male in courtship.

Pythons mate in late winter or early spring. Males may mate every year, while females may only gather the energy to produce eggs every two or three years.

In the breeding season, males may engage in combat, wrestling and biting. A female python may mate several times, with more than one male. The pregnant female may cease eating. When basking, she presents her belly to the sun. In early summer, she lays up to 50 soft-shelled eggs, which clump together when she coils around them, protecting them. In colder weather, she produces some heat by shivering. Incubation may take between five and 15 weeks. At hatching, the young pythons slit their egg cases open, then stay inside for up to 48 hours, absorbing all the yolk before emerging.

DID YOU KNOW?

FACTS

- The Woma, which lives in arid areas of Australia, often hunts in burrows or crevices. It pushes its prey up against a wall to suffocate it.
- The Woma may lure prey by twitching the tip of its tail.
- In the Pilbara of WA, the Olive Python may grow to 6.5 m in length. During hot weather, it may remain submerged in a waterhole.
- The Water Python of coastal northern Australia has been the subject of intensive study near Humpty Doo, NT. A miniature radio transmitter is implanted surgically (using anaesthesia) in a snake's body cavity. Then researchers can follow the snake using radiotelemetry*.

A large python has few enemies but may have parasites like this tick, which will be shed with the skin. Note the heat-sensitive pits on the lip

STANLEY BREEDEN

The Olive Python of northern Australia and Western Australia's Pilbara

STANLEY BREEDEN

The Black-headed Python is a handsome northern snake which feeds mainly on reptiles

BELINDA WRIGHT

The Water Python of northern Australia has water-repellent scales

IAN MORRIS

The desert-living Large-blotched Python rolls in a ball when threatened by a large animal

IAN MORRIS

The large Oenpelli Rock Python is brown during the day and changes to silver-grey at dusk

Heat-seeking missiles

Using the heat-sensitive pits on their faces, most pythons can detect heat radiation differences of as little as 1/30 of a degree Centigrade. They can follow a heat trail or determine the whereabouts of a mammal or bird even in pitch-darkness. The Woma and the Black-headed Python, which feed mainly on reptiles, lack these pits.

FACTS

- The Black-headed Python of northern Australia, which grows to 3 m, lacks heat-sensitive pits. In winter, the black head warms rapidly when exposed to sunlight.
- When harassed, a Large-blotched Python rolls its body into a ball with its head safely concealed inside, presenting a "package" too large for a predator to swallow.
- In the Dry season, Water Pythons hunt rats in the deep cracks in the mud of the Top End floodplains. During the summer Wet season, they become completely aquatic and eat waterbirds and their eggs.

DID YOU KNOW?

FACTS

- Aboriginal people report very large specimens of the Oenpelli Rock Python, a placid Arnhem Land species. It shelters in caves and crevices on the sandstone escarpment and eats mammals and birds.
- The Green Python may use its twitching tailtip as a lure to attract mammals and birds.
- The Amethyst Python (also known as the Scrub Python) lives in forests on the eastern side of Cape York Peninsula. It feeds on mammals, including fruit-bats, gliders and wallabies, and birds.
- There is a record of an Amethyst Python more than 8 m in length. However, no specimen this long exists.
- In winter, a Carpet or Diamond Python may enter a hut, barn or shed and curl up in the rafters, just under the sun-heated roof.
- A Carpet or Diamond Python may slip into a bird cage, swallow its inhabitants, then be unable to squeeze out through the wire or bars it passed easily before eating.

The Diamond Python has a skin decorated with many small pale motifs

Diamond or Carpet?

The Diamond and Carpet Pythons are actually one species. The names are given to differently marked forms living in southwestern, northern and eastern Australia.

These pythons eat mammals and birds and are active mainly at night. One of these snakes will choose an unobtrusive ambush site and wait for prey. If not successful, after several weeks the snake shifts perhaps 100 metres to another place. Even big pythons of this species may remain undetected in outer suburban gardens because of their camouflage and secretive habits. Farmers and graziers welcome them in feed sheds and grain stores because they eat rodents.

PETER SLATER

The Carpet Python has larger blotches in its skin pattern than the Diamond Python

The colours of snakes

Snakes generally seem to have no colour vision. (Some day-hunting species may distinguish red and green.) Their skin colours serve to camouflage them, to confuse prey or to warn possible attackers rather than to communicate with other snakes of the same species. The Green Python is bright yellow, or red, or brown, when young. It changes colour to emerald over a period of between one and 12 weeks, when one to three years of age.

COLUBRID (REAR-FANGED) SNAKES

Less efficient assassins

The Keelback or Freshwater Snake feeds on frogs and tadpoles and can eat Cane Toads without ill effect

The scientific name for the group of rear-fanged snakes is the colubrids. Only 11 of the world's approximately 1600 species of colubrid snakes occur in Australia.

All 11 species are found in the north and northeast of the continent. They are thought to have arrived in Australia from South-East Asia before rising seas submerged the land bridge from New Guinea. Four species of Australia's rear-fanged snakes are aquatic and the remainder live near water or in moist situations.

DID YOU KNOW?

FACTS

- The Eastern Brown Tree Snake ranges in colour from brown with black bands in the south to white with red bands in the northern part of its range. An occasional specimen will be melanistic* (all-black).
- The Northern Brown Tree Snake is also known as the Banded Cat Snake. If molested, it will strike repeatedly, but its fangs are at the rear of its mouth, its venom is weak and its bite is not considered dangerous to humans.

IAN MORRIS

The aquatic Bockadam has nostrils and eyes on the top of its head

A melanistic Eastern Brown Tree Snake

IAN MORRIS

Macleay's Water Snake anchors itself by its tail, waiting to catch fish and frogs

Northern Brown Tree Snake

No threat to humans

No Australian colubrid is regarded as harmful to humans.

Some species of colubrid snakes, including the Bockadam and the Brown Tree Snake, have fangs at the back of the mouth. They do produce venom, but it is weak and they need to get a good grip on the prey before injecting it. The other colubrids, including the arboreal Green Tree and Northern Tree Snakes, the arboreal/terrestrial* Slate-grey Snake and the freshwater Keelback, have only solid teeth – they possess no fangs and no venom glands.

IAN MORRIS

The Green Tree Snake is an agile climber, with a slender body, prehensile tail and keeled belly scales

JIRI LOCHMAN

The Green Tree Snake varies from almost black to pale grey-green with a yellow, green or blue underside

The Green Tree Snake, the best-known Australian colubrid, is found across northern Australia and down the east coast, often in suburban gardens, where it feeds upon frogs and lizards. This non-venomous snake varies in colour. Its back may be bronze, almost black, royal blue, olive or pale grey-green. The underside may range from lemon yellow to green or blue.

FACTS

- The Keelback or Freshwater Snake has been seen to eat young Cane Toads without any apparent ill effect.
- The Keelback moves agilely over mud or aquatic vegetation. Its strong, muscular body flattens and its strongly keeled scales grip even a slippery surface and stop the snake sliding sideways.
- The Bockadam lives in northern tidal creeks and estuaries. Its nostrils have valves and its eyes are set on top of its head. It emits a foul smell in self-defence.
- The female Macleay's Water Snake of the Top End and Cape York gives birth to between 10 and 15 young in the Wet season.
- Colubrid snakes, which lack venom or have weak venom, may swallow their prey alive. The presence of a Green Tree Snake in the garden may be betrayed by cries from unfortunate victims, usually frogs.

DID YOU KNOW?

FACTS ABOUT DEATH ADDERS

- Death adders give warning by flattening the body and flicking from side to side. They may be reluctant to bite. One lay in a gateway on a cane farm all day. At dusk, footprints showed workers had walked across it many times while the snake refrained from striking.
- Death adders vary in colour to match habitats varying from desert sand to forest leaf-litter. Scientists tracking a death adder by radiotelemetry found it very difficult to see the snake even though the radio signal told them exactly where it was lying.

ELAPID (FRONT-FANGED) SNAKES DANGEROUS TO HUMANS

Primed to kill

Australia has 75 of the world's 210 or more species of elapids, or front-fanged snakes. All elapid snakes have sharp, hollow, recurved teeth at the front corners of the upper jaw. The front tooth on each side serves as a fang. When the snake bites, venom from a gland in the upper jaw is forced through it and into the wound. If the fang is damaged, the next tooth takes over its function.

About 20 species of Australian elapids are potentially dangerous to humans. Most prefer to retreat rather than bite, but all will strike if harassed.

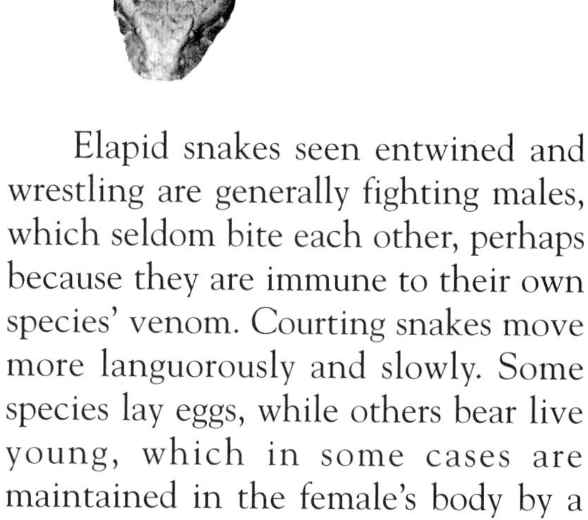
IAN MORRIS

Northern Death Adder

Elapids feed on vertebrate animals and their eggs. Their venom acts upon the nervous and/or circulatory system, and may affect the muscles of the prey in various ways which incapacitate and eventually kill it. It also contains enzymes* which help break down the prey's body tissues ready for the snake to digest.

Many elapid snakes constrict prey as well as biting it. Some release the prey after injecting venom, retrieving it after it stops struggling. Snakes are limbless, fragile creatures and a predator cannot afford to be injured.

Elapid snakes seen entwined and wrestling are generally fighting males, which seldom bite each other, perhaps because they are immune to their own species' venom. Courting snakes move more languorously and slowly. Some species lay eggs, while others bear live young, which in some cases are maintained in the female's body by a placenta.

The Eastern Tiger Snake, which lives in moist habitats, gives birth to live young

Degrees of snakebite

The effect of a snakebite on a human can vary from a minor problem to being lethal, depending on a number of factors:

- The type of snake
- The nature of its venom
- The amount of venom injected (which depends on whether the snake struck while feeding, or while defending itself)
- The size and state of health of the victim
- The availability of first aid or proper medical care

The Dugite of southwestern Western Australia

The Mulga Snake produces copious venom

The three species of copperhead, including this Lowlands Copperhead, prefer cool habitats

The Red-bellied Black Snake inhabits moist places in coastal eastern Australia

Potentially lethal

The bite of any of the following front-fanged snakes could be potentially lethal to a human:

Southern Death Adder
Northern Death Adder
Desert Death Adder
Pygmy Copperhead
Highlands Copperhead
Lowlands Copperhead
Small-eyed Snake
Black Tiger Snake
Eastern Tiger Snake
Western Tiger Snake
Taipan
Inland Taipan
Mulga Snake
Spotted Mulga Snake
Collett's Black Snake
Spotted Black Snake
Red-bellied Black Snake
Dugite
Eastern Brown Snake
Western Brown Snake
Rough-scaled Snake

Effects of snake venoms

It is to a snake's advantage if its venom stops the prey moving in a short time, allowing it to be retrieved and swallowed without danger to the snake. The venom should also prepare the prey's tissues for easy digestion.

Injected snake venom may act on the victim's body in a number of ways. and the venom of one species may contain several separate lethal agents.

- Coagulants cause blood to clot.
- Anticoagulants prevent blood clotting.
- Neurotoxins act on the nervous system, causing paralysis.
- Myotoxins affect the muscles, causing paralysis and kidney failure.
- Other agents in venom may cause red blood cells to break down, or blood platelets to clump.

The shy Ringed Brown Snake avoids humans. Its five to 12 black bands tend to fade with age

FACTS

- The Taipan of northern and northeastern Australia is a swift, lethal hunter of mammals (especially rodents). Large prey is bitten, allowed to escape (it doesn't get far), then retrieved after it dies.

The Western Carpentaria Snake is a night hunter

- In defensive pose, a Mulga Snake inflates its body, then swings the flattened neck and forebody from side to side. It produces a large amount of venom and its bite may be fatal.
- The Mulga Snake lives in most arid and semi-arid parts of the continent.

Less harmful to humans

IAN MORRIS

Southern Shovel-nosed Snake

All snakes in the elapid group have fangs at the fronts of their mouths and venom glands. However, many species are very small and produce little venom. Some have only weak venom, some have very short fangs and many are reluctant to bite. They may combine some or all of these traits and, except for large individuals of some species, which should be treated with caution, are not usually dangerous to humans.

Note that reaction to a bite from any elapid snake, no matter how small, should be assessed by a medical practitioner.

Like their more potent relatives, the less dangerous elapid snakes kill their prey by a combination of the action of venom and by constriction. Often they eat reptiles, especially skinks.

Some of these elapids are extremely limited in distribution (e.g. the Broad-headed Snake, a threatened species), while others have a wide distribution (e.g. the Yellow-faced Whipsnake). Many of the smaller elapid species are burrowers, seldom seen unless earth is turned, or unless the snake ventures to the surface after rain or at nightfall.

IAN MORRIS

The Grey Whipsnake of the Kimberley, WA

IAN MORRIS

The Northern Bandy-bandy preys on blind snakes

The rare Stephen's Banded Snake bears live young

IAN MORRIS

The Spotted Snake of northern Australia

DID YOU KNOW?

FACTS

- Whipsnakes are big-eyed, day-hunting, very agile snakes. They have smooth, matt scales and often a dark, comma-like marking below each eye. There are nine Australian species and our "fastest" snake is probably a whipsnake.
- The Grey Whipsnake is a small, thick-bodied whipsnake, growing to just over 50 cm in length, which is found in sandstone country in the Kimberley, WA.
- Stephen's Banded Snake is a rare climbing snake of coastal northern NSW and southern Qld. It shelters in tree and rock crevices and eats small animals. The female bears three to eight live young.
- The two species of Bandy-bandy feed exclusively on blind snakes. One may swallow a victim as large as its own body.
- The Spotted Snake of northern and central Australia forages for lizards and blind snakes at night. It grows to just over 60 cm and shelters in soil cracks, under rocks and in animal burrows.

THE HEAD-BASKERS

JIRI LOCHMAN

The Black-striped Burrowing Snake, found only around Perth, WA, eats skinks and legless lizards

JIRI LOCHMAN

Gould's Hooded Snake

IAN MORRIS

Unbanded Shovel-nosed Snake

On a cool morning, a snake with dark scales on its crown and nape often pushes its head out into the sunlight, warming it (and the brain) before emerging from shelter. Sunlight falling on a dark line down the snake's spine may also help warm up the reptile's central nervous system, overcoming sluggishness caused by cold.

Banded confusion

Many small elapids have strongly striped bodies and hunt at dusk and during the first hours of darkness.

It is difficult to form an accurate mental image of a moving body covered by alternating light and dark rings (for a similar confusing effect, drive down a road striped with tree-shadow and sunshine).This "flicker-fusion" effect presumably helps conceal banded snakes from their prey.

Sydney's rare snake

The Broad-headed Snake lives only in the Sydney basin, sheltering in crevices and under ledges and flakes of Hawkesbury sandstone. It is endangered as its habitat is being "tidied" by rock removal and many areas are disappearing under housing. This snake is said to urge a lizard towards its mouth by encircling the victim with its tail.

FACTS

- Gould's Hooded Snake occurs in southwestern Australia. It feeds on skinks, geckos and legless lizards and females give birth to three to seven young. It is a "head-basker", extending the dark head into sunlight to raise the temperature of head and brain.
- The rare Unbanded Shovel-nosed Snake has smooth, glossy scales and is a "head-basker". It swims through loose sand and can reverse for about half its body length without disturbing the soil surface.
- The White-lipped Snake is Australia's most cold-adapted snake. It lives on Mount Kosciusko and in the Australian Alps and also in Tasmania, where it is larger than on the mainland.

JIRI LOCHMAN

Yellow-faced Whipsnake

DID YOU KNOW?

FACTS

- Seasnakes are thought to have common ancestors with the elapid snakes.
- In some species of seasnake, the scales of the male are much more keeled than those of the female, perhaps to give him a firmer grip during mating. This activity takes place in the water and the young are born underwater.
- Some seasnakes can dive to 100 m and may remain submerged for up to 80 minutes. They do not appear to suffer from "the bends" after surfacing.
- As the Yellow-bellied Seasnake drifts across the ocean, small fish may gather under it, as they do under any floating object. Eventually the snake swims backwards and snaps sideways at the fish around its head.
- The circulation of fish is sluggish compared to that of warm-blooded mammals. Seasnakes need to hold on to their victims to give their venom the best chance to take effect.

Living offshore

Thirty-two species of seasnake are recorded from Australia's coastal waters. These wholly aquatic snakes may grow to two metres in length and have deep, narrow bodies. Their tails are compressed from side to side to form paddles.

A seasnake swims by undulating the body from side to side. Some species can swim backwards. The nostrils are on the top of the snout and have flaps that close when the snake submerges. Air is taken into the body through the nostrils, but some oxygen/carbon dioxide exchange takes place between water and bloodstream through the skin. A gland under the snake's tongue removes excess salt from the blood and excretes it.

Golden Seasnake is found around the northern half of Australia

NEIL WEHLACK (LOCHMAN TRANSPARENCIES)

Seasnakes' scales range from overlapping to small and non-overlapping. Some scales bear spines or are keeled. Rough scales may help the snake hold slippery prey long enough for venom to take effect.

The usual prey of seasnakes is fish, or fish eggs, detected by taste and possibly by sensing vibration through the water. The venom fangs and glands are similar to those of elapid snakes and the venom is particularly toxic in some fish-catching species. Any seasnake bite should be treated with caution. First aid should be applied and medical advice sought.

When this Golden Seasnake enters a crevice, an area on its tail registers whether it is still exposed to light

"Seeing" with its tail

The Golden (sometimes called the Olive) Seasnake is a stout-bodied snake which can grow to over two metres in length. It is found in coastal waters around the northern half of Australia, usually at depths of between five and 20 metres. It has an area in its tail which is sensitive to light. When the snake takes refuge in a coral crevice during the daytime, it may be able to tell through signals received from this area whether its tail is safely hidden from predators.

GEOFF TAYLOR

A Golden Seasnake (head at top left) swallowing an eel

IAN MORRIS

Turtle-headed Seasnake resting

EVA BOOGAARD

Stokes's Seasnake swallowing prey

Sea kraits

Like seasnakes, sea kraits probably evolved from elapid ancestors. However, they are not so tied to the ocean as seasnakes and come to land to bask, to shelter and to lay their eggs in crevices or under litter. Their body scales are smooth and overlapping; their bodies are less compressed from side to side than those of seasnakes and their tails are paddle-like.

Sea kraits are found in water less than ten metres in depth, near coral reefs or islands, usually well offshore. They forage for eels and fish underwater, in reef crevices. Their venom is potent.

The Wide-faced Sea Krait and the Large-scaled Sea Krait may occur in remote Barrier Reef waters. Both are strongly banded with black.

IAN MORRIS

The Wide-faced Sea Krait moves to and from the land during nocturnal high tides

FACTS

- The Golden Seasnake probes into crevices in coral for fish, crabs, prawns and eels. A loop of the body may be used to block prey in its refuge. The female gives birth to between one and five young.
- Stokes's Seasnake has a keel of scales along the underside of its body. The bulkiest of the seasnakes, it forages around reefs and the sea floor for fish. It is fairly common in Australian waters.
- Sea kraits have very large lungs, which enable them to stay underwater for long periods. They also have nostrils which are closed by valves, and salt-excreting glands under their tongues.
- Female sea kraits are much larger than males of the same species and tend to hunt in deeper waters.
- Sea kraits grow to about 1.4 m in length.

Creatures of legend

For the Aboriginal people, snakes were both vital elements of culture and sources of food. For early European settlers, snakes were nuisances and threats. Today, they are frightening bogies to many Australians who may never see even one snake in its natural habitat.

This Bardick is warning that if provoked any further it may strike

JIRI LOCHMAN

Most of Australia's snakes threaten only the small creatures on which they prey. Some of the most commonly seen snakes are non-venomous. Only a small proportion of the venomous snakes have the potential to kill a human and bites are rare unless the snake is harassed. Only one or two people are killed by snakebite in Australia each year. However, even one fatality is too many.

If possible, leave a snake alone if it does not threaten you or yours.

It is useful to know which snakes are potentially harmful and which are harmless (and which are legless lizards or skinks with reduced limbs). It also pays to know how to deal with snakebite if it occurs.

Use an elastic bandage!

Snake venom passes through body tissues and collects in the lymph vessels* before being carried into the bloodstream. An elastic bandage wrapped firmly around a bitten limb delays the venom passing into the bloodstream. Remember that symptoms may appear suddenly once the bandage is unwrapped.

This method replaces any previous methods of on-the-spot treatment of snakebite (or suspected snakebite).

Always have an elastic bandage handy in the bush. Wear protective clothing when bushwalking. A mobile phone can be useful to ask advice and to alert medical help.

DID YOU KNOW?

HOW TO AVOID PROBLEMS WITH SNAKES

- Learn about snakes so you can tell a harmless species from a potentially harmful one.
- Watch out for snakes in moist situations, near piles of timber, or under pieces of roofing iron lying on the ground.
- Keep your lawn trimmed and yard free of debris. Clear away domestic rubbish. Be aware that mice and frogs attract snakes.
- When you see a snake, leave it alone. Educate your family not to interfere with snakes. Keep domestic animals away from snakes.
- The heavier your footstep, the less likely you are to see a snake.

The Taipan is one of Australia's deadliest snakes

A bite from a Yellow-faced Whipsnake may cause pain but is not potentially lethal to humans

JIRI LOCHMAN

IF SNAKEBITE OCCURS

- **Stay calm and keep others calm.** Identify the snake if possible, but don't waste time chasing it.
- **Don't wash or wipe the wound.** The snake can be identified from venom traces, and this will enable treatment to be specific.
- **Stop venom reaching the general circulation** by wrapping an elastic bandage firmly around the bitten limb. Then elevate the limb and splint it.
- **If the bite is on the trunk or head,** keep the patient as still as possible.
- **Take the patient to the nearest medical facility,** telephoning in advance if possible. If necessary, bring medical help to the patient.
- **Don't remove the elastic bandage until medical help is at hand.**

DENNIS SARSON

Ready to milk venom from a tiger snake

DENNIS SARSON

The snake bites a membrane and venom collects in the vessel

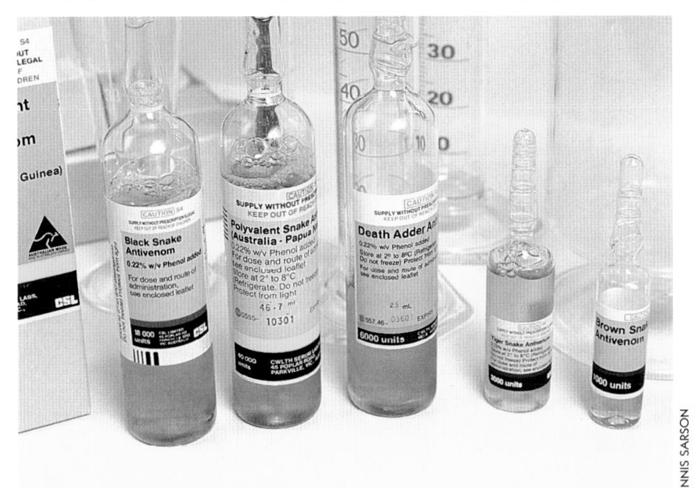

DENNIS SARSON

Assorted snakebite antivenoms

Which is "most dangerous"?

The Inland Taipan is Australia's most venomous snake. It is therefore, strictly speaking, Australia's most dangerous snake.

However, this shy, inland species rates as less of a potential danger than the Taipan. This has less potent venom, but is easily provoked, has large amounts of venom and very long fangs. It also lives in areas increasingly invaded by humans who wear little protective clothing.

The Mulga (King Brown) Snake has by far the largest venom yield of any Australian snake.

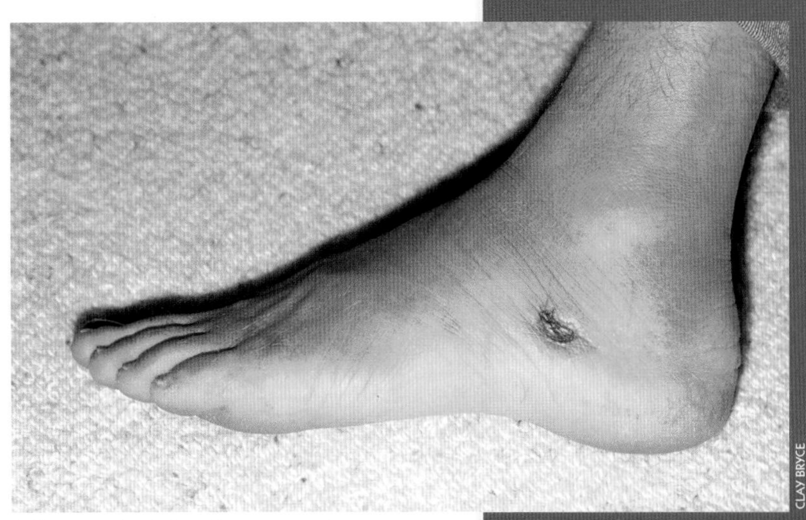

CLAY BRYCE

A tiger snake bite after seven days

FACTS ABOUT ANTIVENOM

- The first antivenom* for an Australian species of snake was developed for the tiger snake in 1929 by Charles Halliley Kellaway, in Melbourne. Taipan antivenom was produced in 1955.
- Antivenom is horse blood serum which contains antibodies to the venom of a particular snake. It must be refrigerated for storage.
- Some people have an allergic reaction to antivenom. It should be administered only by a qualified medical practitioner who can treat the reaction if necessary.
- Antivenom should not be injected unless symptoms from snakebite appear.

What is happening to Australia's reptiles?

Reptiles were traditional items of diet for some Aboriginal people. Until 1788, changes in the status of reptile species were gradual, or limited in extent. Today, many of Australia's reptiles are still abundant and widespread. However, some species are rare, threatened or endangered.

It is comparatively easy to judge the welfare of large species. The Saltwater Crocodile is increasing in numbers and indeed is being "farmed", but the sea turtles are under extreme pressure worldwide, largely through hunting, nest site destruction and deaths in trawling nets.

Patient detective work is needed, however, to discover the status of small, inconspicuous reptile species.

Habitat destruction, which eliminates the cover and food sources necessary for reptile survival, is a major cause of reptile decline in many areas. Reptiles occupying limited habitats exploited by humans, like the Broad-headed Snake of the Sydney sandstone belt, Western Australia's Western Swamp Turtle and the recently rediscovered Adelaide Pygmy Blue-tongue, are endangered.

The domestic and the feral cat, the feral fox and the Cane Toad have added yet more pressure on Australia's reptile populations. All are predators, and the Cane Toad poisons nearly all reptiles which attempt to eat it. On a smaller scale, snakes are often the direct victims of human prejudice, and legless lizards, which are superficially snake-like, are killed because of the resemblance.

IAN MORRIS

How can we help reptiles survive?

- Learn as much as you can about reptiles. Knowledge is power and drives out fear. Learn that reptiles are not "slimy" but dry, often warm, exotically beautiful creatures.
- Support movements to conserve natural bushland and help prevent bushfires. Allowing reptile habitat to remain helps preserve reptiles.
- Leave snakes alone if it is possible to do so. Stand back and the snake should go away. If it doesn't, *you* go away.
- If you can safely do so, avoid running over reptiles basking on, or crossing, the road.
- If you don't like reptiles, do not create conditions which attract them. Rodent-eaters are attracted to rats and mice; frog-eaters frequent ponds.
- If your bird cage contains a fat Carpet Python but no more budgies, be philosophical and merciful.
- Be careful with pesticides and herbicides, which poison prey which poisons reptiles.
- Exterminate Cane Toads.
- Know that each year many reptiles die during illegal attempts to smuggle them out of the country.
- Be aware that reptiles can live successfully in suburban surroundings and leave some "wilderness" on your house block. It might be home to skinks, geckos, harmless blind snakes and, if you are lucky and live in warmer parts of Australia, a gorgeous prize such as a Carpet Python, Blue-tongued Skink or Eastern Water Dragon.

Glossary

aestivate. To become inactive during summer drought. Survival tactic used by some freshwater turtles and frogs.

amphibian. Four-limbed, ectothermic vertebrate with moist, non-scaly skin. Immature stage usually aquatic.

amplexus. Amphibian mating embrace; male grasps female around her groin or armpits with his front legs.

anaerobic. Without using oxygen.

antivenom. Immunised horse-blood serum injected into victim of a venomous bite to counteract its effects.

arboreal. Living in trees.

ballast. Heavy material used to help an animal or vessel remain stable in air or water.

carapace. Upper part of a turtle's shell.

carnivorous. Eating mainly other animals.

cartilage. Gristle; skeletal connective tissue.

cloaca. Final part of gut in amphibians, reptiles, birds and monotremes. Receives reproductive cells, urine and digestive wastes.

colubrids. Large worldwide family of snakes having both jaws with solid or grooved teeth; most species harmless, a few venomous.

dehydration. Condition in which an organism suffers from inadequate water in tissues.

dentition. Type, number and arrangement of teeth found in a particular animal or group of animals.

ecological niche. The particular place an animal or plant occupies in an environment.

ectothermic. Referring to an animal whose body temperature remains close to the temperature of its environment; all animals except for birds and mammals.

elapids. Family of snakes with short, stout, erect fangs, some adapted to transmit venom. Elapids dominate snake species in the southern part of Australia.

enzymes. Substances which speed chemical reactions.

fossil. Remains or traces of a once-living organism.

genus. Group of animals containing a number of species with similar characteristics.

gills. Structures in fish and water-living amphibians through which exchange of respiratory gases takes place.

glandular. Containing glands.

glottis. Opening to windpipe.

granular. Covered with bumps.

hemipenes. Paired organs used by some male reptiles to place their sperm within females of the same species.

herpetologist. Person who studies reptiles.

hibernate. Remain inactive during cold periods.

incubation. Process in which eggs are kept at a temperature which allows them to develop and hatch.

intercalary structure. Piece of cartilage situated between the final two bones of the digits of some frogs.

invertebrates. Animals without backbones.

labyrinthodonts. Group of ancient amphibians, so-called because of the wrinkled surfaces of their teeth.

ligaments. Bands of fibrous tissue which join bones.

live-bearers. Animals whose young are born unprotected by eggshell or tough membrane.

lymph vessels. Network of vessels carrying lymph, a clear fluid containing white blood cells, around the body.

macrocephalic. Possessing a larger-than-normal head.

mammals. Warm-blooded vertebrate animals which have hair and feed their young on milk.

melanistic. Dark-coloured due to black melanin pigment. A term used of darker than normal individuals.

metamorphosis. Abrupt, dramatic or total transformation from one stage in an animal's life to another, e.g. tadpole to frog.

nocturnal. Active at night.

osteoderms. Bony plates found beneath skin of crocodilians and some turtles.

oxygen debt. High level of oxygen consumption necessary after exertion with inadequate oxygen.

parthenogenetic. Reproduction by unfertilised female.

pigment. Colouring substance. In animals, pigment is usually black, brown, yellow, red or white.

placentas. Structures connecting circulatory systems of unborn infants to those of their mothers.

plastron. Lower part of a turtle's shell.

predators. Animals which kill and eat other animals.

prehensile. Adapted for grasping by curling around.

radioactive. Emitting radiation as atomic nuclei within the substance break down.

radiotelemetry. Tracing an animal by tracking emissions from a radio which has been attached to it externally or inserted internally.

retina. Innermost nervous tissue layer of the eyeball.

scutes. External bony plates.

shunt. Structure in blood vessel which diverts blood from one part of the body to another.

species. Group of animals which can breed together and produce fertile offspring.

terrestrial. Living on the ground.

torpid. Inactive and sluggish.

toxic. Poisonous.

toxin. Poison of animal or vegetable origin.

tubercles. Small conical bumps.

tympanum. Membranous eardrum, visible in some frogs and lizards.

vegetarian. Eating mainly plant material.

venom. Poisonous fluid produced by reptiles, scorpions, insects and other animals.

vertebrae. Bones which make up the backbone, or vertebral column.

vertebrate. Animal with a backbone surrounding the spinal cord and a skull protecting the brain.

vomerine teeth. Two patches of teeth on the vomerine bones in the front part of the roof of the mouth; especially in amphibians and reptiles.

Map

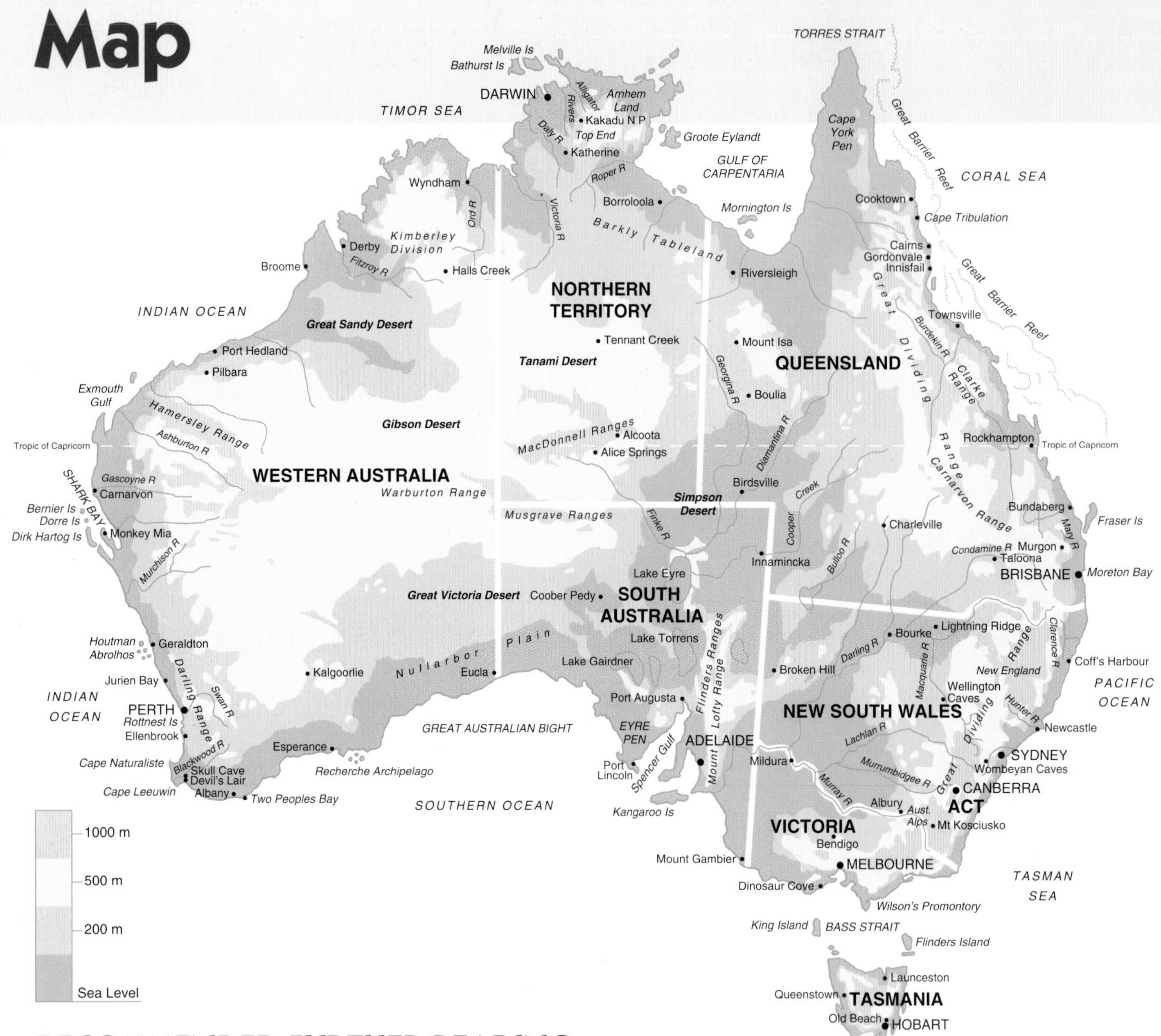

RECOMMENDED FURTHER READING

BARKER, GRIGG & TYLER, 1995. *A Field Guide to Australian Frogs*. Surrey Beatty & Sons, Sydney.

COGGER, H.G., 1992. *Reptiles and Amphibians of Australia*. Revised edition. A.H. & A.W. Reed, Sydney.

GOW, G.F., 1989. *Complete Guide to Australian Snakes*. Cornstalk (Collins Angus & Robertson), Sydney.

EHMANN, H., 1992. *The Australian Museum Encyclopedia of Australian Animals: Reptiles*. Angus & Robertson, Sydney.

MIRTSCHIN, P. and DAVID, R., 1992. *Snakes of Australia*. Hill of Content, Melbourne.

MUSEUMS OF VARIOUS STATES: Any publications on frogs or reptiles, by various authors.

QUEENSLAND DEPARTMENT OF THE ENVIRONMENT AND HERITAGE. *A Matter of Time: Sea Turtles of Queensland*. Brisbane.

SHINE, RICK, 1993. *Australian Snakes: A Natural History*, Reed Books, Sydney.

TYLER, M., 1994. *Australian Frogs: A Natural History*. Reed Books, Sydney.

TYLER, M., 1992. *The Australian Museum Encyclopedia of Australian Animals: Frogs*. Angus & Robertson, Sydney.

WEBB G. and MANOLIS, C., 1989. *Crocodiles of Australia*. Reed Books. Sydney.

WILSON, K.W. and KNOWLES, D.G., 1988. *Australia's Reptiles: A Photographic Reference to the Terrestrial Reptiles of Australia*. Cornstalk (Collins Angus & Robertson), Sydney

PHOTOGRAPHY: Steve Parish (uncredited photographs) and Australia's finest wildlife photographers: Ian Morris, Jiri Lochman, Stanley Breeden, Peter Slater, Marie Lochman, Belinda Wright, Owen Kelly, Pat Slater, Raoul Slater, Peter Marsack, Eva Boogaard, Dennis Sarson, Geoff Taylor, Clay Bryce, as credited.

ACKNOWLEDGEMENTS: Thanks are due to Ian Morris and the staff of the Queensland Museum for their helpful comments.

First published in Australia by Steve Parish Publishing Pty Ltd
PO BOx 1058, Archerfield BC, Queensland 4108 Australia

www.steveparish.com.au

ISBN 1-875932-33-X

Series designed by Leanne Nobilio, SPP
Cover designed by Leanne Staff, SPP
Printed in Singapore